D1265677

Matrix Algebra
for
Physicists

MATRIX ALGEBRA FOR PHYSICISTS

R. K. EISENSCHITZ, DR.PHIL., D.SC., F.INST.P.
Professor Em. of Theoretical Physics
University of London

PLENUM PRESS
NEW YORK
1966

U.S. edition published by
PLENUM PRESS
227 West 17th Street
New York, New York 10011

Library of Congress Catalog Card Number 66-18972

Second Printing–January, 1967

Printed in the United States

Preface

This introduction to matrix algebra will be found of particular value to students working for B.Sc. and similar examinations.

The matrix algebra commonly used in physics is presented in Chapters 1–7, but for a preliminary survey it is sufficient to consider only Sections 1–5, 7, 11, 15, 16, 19–23 and 25.

Readers are assumed to have an elementary knowledge of vectors and complex numbers. Apart from that, arguments involve hardly anything but addition and multiplication.

The application of matrices to various fields of physics is presented in the second half of the book. A number of examples are worked out in detail. They require a fair knowledge of the calculus; in some places even Fourier transforms and contour integration are used. No instructions for this kind of analysis are given since it happens to be better known than algebraic methods, even though the latter are more elementary.

CONTENTS

CHAPTER 1

VECTORS

1. Definition

The mathematics presented in this volume are concerned with entities distinct from simple numbers. They require for their specification ordered sets of numbers rather than a single number. Ordinary vectors are entities of this kind: they are usually thought of as having a well-defined length and orientation and are denoted by arrows. In the present context it is more important to think of vectors in terms of their Cartesian components. A single vector is a concise expression for three quantities and an equation between vectors conveys the information otherwise conveyed by three equations. By the use of vectors mathematical expressions are reduced in length, numbers of equations are diminished and the content of mathematical arguments is given greater clarity by the shedding of inessentials.

The technique of substituting a single symbol for specified sets of quantities is by no means restricted to vectors. It is of particular use if applied to entities which require a large number of quantities for their specification. The mathematics of these entities might be unmanageable without the use of some formalism by which cumbersome expressions are contracted. Part of the formalism consists in rules for combining symbols, similar to the rules of vector algebra.

In this volume we consider entities called 'vectors' (a generalization of the familiar concept) and 'matrices'. Entities of this kind play an increasingly important part in contemporary physics.

The rules by which vectors and matrices are combined are concise prescriptions which indicate repeated additions and multiplications. The subject is accordingly of an elementary character. Its only 'advanced' aspect is the continual use of complex numbers. Results of geometry or of the calculus enter only into subsidiary arguments and into applications.

The subject is conveniently started by the definition of 'abstract vectors' (or just 'vectors') which are a generalization of the familiar space vectors.

DEFINITION (1.A) A 'vector in n dimensions' is an ordered set of n real or complex numbers to which are applied certain well-defined rules. The numbers themselves are called components of the vector.

If in a set of vectors some particular component or components of every vector should vanish the number of dimensions of these vectors might be ambiguous. This ambiguity will not affect any conclusions to be derived. It is convenient to define a null vector the components of which are zero throughout. Its dimension is consistent with the context in which it appears and it is usually denoted by O.

Vectors are specified by writing the components in the appropriate order in a row or in a column. At a later stage it will sometimes be necessary to distinguish between row and column vectors. In general terms the components can be denoted by subscripts such as a_1, $a_2 \ldots a_n$. A concise notation for a vector is called for; a bold faced letter will be used. Thus **a** denotes a vector, in particular a column vector; the corresponding row vector is denoted by $\tilde{\mathbf{a}}$.

As an example the two sets 1, 2, 3, 4, 5 and 1, 3, 2, 4, 5 can be regarded as vectors in 5 dimensions; they are distinct by the order of the components although the numerical values of the components are the same.

The term 'scalar' will occasionally be applied to numbers in order to distinguish them from vectors. Rules for calculating with vectors will be laid down by definition. Although this procedure may be axiomatic, the rules will nevertheless be readily accepted since they are familiar when applied to space vectors.

DEFINITION (1.B) A vector is multiplied by a scalar by multiplying every single component of the vector by that scalar. The result is a vector.

Thus $\mathbf{c} = \lambda\mathbf{a}$ has the components $c_j = \lambda a_j \quad (j = 1, 2 \ldots n)$.

DEFINITION (1.C) Two vectors are added by adding corresponding components. The result is a vector.

Thus $\mathbf{p} = \mathbf{r} + \mathbf{s}$ has the components $p_j = r_j + s_j \quad (j = 1, 2 \ldots n)$.

In specifying a vector the components can be written as the coefficients of a polynomial or some other series. Thus the polynomial

$$a_1 x + a_2 x^2 + \ldots + a_n x^n$$

can be regarded as a vector with the components a_j. The meaning of the variable x is of minor significance. This representation has the advantage of complying automatically with the rules (1.B) and (1.C) if a polynomial is multiplied by a number or two polynomials are added.

The importance of space vectors in physics is common knowledge. Vectors other than space vectors are used in various contexts. If, for example, a quantity x is a periodic function of the time t with the period τ it can be expanded in a series

$$x(t) = \sum_j b_j \exp(-2\pi itj/\tau) \tag{1.1}$$

If two series of the form (1.1) with different coefficients but the same period are added or if one series is multiplied by a number the result is a different time function with the same period. Here the coefficients b_j are conveniently regarded as components of a vector. If this formula is applied to a vibrating string it is seen that the amplitudes of the different harmonics are instances of an abstract vector. Generally the concept of vectors will be applied to sets of numbers for which addition in accordance with (1.C) has a meaning in physics.

The concept of vectors may be generalized in such a way that vector components need not necessarily be numbers but can be entities of a different kind; examples are given in Sections 37 and 45.

2. Linear dependence

Given a set of vectors new vectors can be derived by multiplying the original vectors by scalars and then adding. The resulting vectors are called linear combinations of the original vectors. The vector $(-6, 3, 0, 3)$, for example, is a linear combination of $(-2, 1, -1, 2)$ and $(2, -1, -2, 1)$ obtained by multiplying the first vector by 2, the second by -1, and adding.

A linear combination of vectors may be a null vector even if the vectors themselves are non-zero. This possibility will now be investigated in some detail.

First consider space vectors. Two vectors determine the orientation of a plane to which both are parallel. The sum of these vectors is also parallel to the plane. Multiplication of the two vectors can—if negative factors are used—change the direction of the vectors within the plane but the orientation of the plane would not be affected. It follows that all linear combinations of the two vectors are parallel to one and the same plane.

A vector which is not parallel to the plane cannot be parallel to any linear combination of the two original vectors. Thus three space vectors which are not coplanar cannot form a vanishing linear combination. On the other hand it is plausible to assume that three coplanar space vectors can form a vanishing linear combination. This will eventually be proved.

In fact, two forces acting on a point can be balanced by a force parallel to the same plane, whatever the magnitude of the forces may be; they could not be balanced by a force which is not parallel to the plane of the two other forces.

Turning now to abstract vectors let $\mathbf{a}^{(1)}$, $\mathbf{a}^{(2)} \ldots \mathbf{a}^{(R)}$, and $q^{(1)}$, $q^{(2)} \ldots q^{(R)}$ be a set of vectors and of scalars respectively.

DEFINITION (2.A) If the numbers $q^{(r)}$ can be chosen in such a way that the linear combination

$$q^{(1)}\mathbf{a}^{(1)} + q^{(2)}\mathbf{a}^{(2)} + \ldots + q^{(R)}\mathbf{a}^{(R)} = \mathrm{O}$$

the vectors are said to be linearly dependent. If a choice of this kind is impossible the vectors are 'linearly independent'.

In this definition it is understood that not all of the $q^{(r)}$ are zero.

THEOREM (2.B) $n + 1$ vectors in n dimensions are linearly dependent.

This is proved by induction. It is assumed that the theorem has been established for n vectors in $n - 1$ dimensions; its validity for $n + 1$ vectors in n dimensions is deduced.

If n out of the $n + 1$ vectors are linearly dependent the theorem is proved by choosing n out of the $n + 1$ scalars $q^{(r)}$ in such a way that the corresponding linear combination of n vectors vanishes; the remaining scalar $q^{(r)}$ is made zero.

If all sets of n vectors are linearly independent then there must be at least one out of $n + 1$ vectors which has a non-vanishing first component. If that were not so, all $n + 1$ vectors would have only $n - 1$ non-vanishing components and could not be distinguished from vectors in $n - 1$ dimensions; they would be linearly dependent by premises. The vectors are labelled or, if necessary, will be re-labelled in such a way that the component $a_1^{(n+1)}$ does not vanish.

A new set of vectors is now defined:

$$\mathbf{b}^{(r)} = a_1^{(n+1)}\mathbf{a}^{(r)} - a_1^{(r)}\mathbf{a}^{(n+1)} \quad (r = 1, 2 \ldots n) \tag{2.1}$$

The first components of these vectors vanish:

$$b_1^{(r)} = a_1^{(n+1)}a_1^{(r)} - a_1^{(r)}a_1{}^{(n+1)} = 0$$

According to premises the n vectors $\mathbf{b}^{(r)}$ are linearly dependent. It is accordingly possible to choose the numbers $p^{(1)}, p^{(2)} \ldots p^{(n)}$ in such a way that

$$\sum_{r=1}^{n} p^{(r)}\mathbf{b}^{(r)} = \sum_{r=1}^{n} p^{(r)}[a_1^{(n+1)}\mathbf{a}^{(r)} - a_1^{(r)}\mathbf{a}^{(n+1)}] = 0$$

Hence by putting

$$q^{(r)} = p^{(r)}a_1^{(n+1)} \quad (r = 1, 2 \ldots n)$$

$$q^{(n+1)} = -\sum_{r=1}^{n} p^{(r)}a_1^{(r)}$$

a vanishing linear combination of the vectors $\mathbf{a}^{(r)}$ can be constructed, thus completing the induction proof.

In order to prove theorem (2.B) it is sufficient to show that it is true for two vectors in one dimension. If c and d are vectors in one dimension their linear combination gives

$$q^{(1)}c + q^{(2)}d = 0, \quad \text{if } q^{(2)}/q^{(1)} = -c/d$$

Theorem (2.B) is accordingly shown to be valid.

A corollary of (2.B) is that three coplanar space vectors are linearly dependent whereas in general three space vectors are linearly independent.

As the proof of theorem (2.B) involves rather abstract reasoning the argument is now illustrated by an example. Consider five vectors in four dimensions.

$$\begin{aligned} \mathbf{a}^{(1)} &= (-1, 1, 1, 1) \qquad \mathbf{a}^{(2)} = (1, -1, 1, 1) \\ \mathbf{a}^{(3)} &= (1, 1, -1, 1) \qquad \mathbf{a}^{(4)} = (1, 1, 1, -1) \\ &\qquad \mathbf{a}^{(5)} = (1, 1, 1, 1) \end{aligned} \tag{2.2}$$

Then, by (2.1)

$$\begin{aligned} \mathbf{b}^{(1)} &= \mathbf{a}^{(1)} + \mathbf{a}^{(5)} = (0, 2, 2, 2) \\ \mathbf{b}^{(2)} &= \mathbf{a}^{(2)} - \mathbf{a}^{(5)} = (0, -2, 0, 0) \\ \mathbf{b}^{(3)} &= \mathbf{a}^{(3)} - \mathbf{a}^{(5)} = (0, 0, -2, 0) \\ \mathbf{b}^{(4)} &= \mathbf{a}^{(4)} - \mathbf{a}^{(5)} = (0, 0, 0, -2) \end{aligned}$$

It is readily verified that the linear combination

$$\mathbf{b}^{(1)} + \mathbf{b}^{(2)} + \mathbf{b}^{(3)} + \mathbf{b}^{(4)} = 0$$

and that

$$q^{(1)} = q^{(2)} = q^{(3)} = q^{(4)} = 1, \quad q^{(5)} = -2$$

n vectors or any smaller number of vectors in n dimensions may be linearly independent or dependent. So far no criterion has been given for deciding this alternative.

If n linearly independent vectors in n dimensions are given it follows from theorem (2.B) that every vector in n dimensions can be represented as a linear combination of these vectors. The representation is of particularly simple form if the following basic vectors are used

$$\left.\begin{aligned} \mathbf{e}^{(1)} &= (1, 0 \ldots 0) \\ \mathbf{e}^{(2)} &= (0, 1 \ldots 0) \\ &\vdots \\ \mathbf{e}^{(n)} &= (0, 0 \ldots 1) \end{aligned}\right\} \tag{2.3}$$

In representing any vector $\mathbf{a}$ as a linear combination of these basic vectors the coefficients are equal to the components a_r.

3. Scalar product: Orthogonality

The scalar product of two space vectors is defined as the product of their magnitudes and the cosine of the angle between them. It is equal to the sum of the products of their corresponding Cartesian components. If the vectors are perpendicular to each other the scalar product vanishes whatever the magnitudes of the vectors may be. The scalar product of a vector by itself is the square of the magnitude of the vector.

Similar statements can be made with respect to abstract vectors. If the scalar product of two column vectors **a** and **b** is denoted by **(ab)**,

$$(\mathbf{ab}) = \sum_{j=1}^{n} a_j^* b_j \tag{3.1}$$

where the asterisk denotes the conjugate complex.

Readers are reminded that the conjugate complex of the number $\alpha + i\beta$ is $\alpha - i\beta$ (α, β being real) and *vice versa*, and the conjugate complex of a product of two complex numbers is the product of the conjugate complex factors, i.e.

$$[(\alpha + i\beta)(\gamma + i\eta)]^* = (\alpha - i\beta)(\gamma - i\eta)$$

The inequality of Schwarz

If **a** and **b** are vectors then

$$|(\mathbf{ab})|^2 \leqslant a^2 b^2 \tag{3.2}$$

This relation can be used for finding an upper limit for scalar products. In order to prove (3.2) let

$$\begin{aligned} S &= a^2 b^2 - |(\mathbf{ab})|^2 \qquad (3.3) \\ &= \sum_{j,k} [|a_j|^2 |b_k|^2 - a_j^* b_j a_k b_k^*] \end{aligned}$$

and

$$\begin{aligned} T &= \sum_{j,k} |a_j b_k - a_k b_j|^2 \qquad (3.4) \\ &= \sum_{j,k} (a_j b_k - a_k b_j)(a_j^* b_k^* - a_k^* b_j^*) \\ &= \sum_{j,k} [|a_j|^2 |b_k|^2 + |a_k|^2 |b_j|^2 - a_j^* a_k b_j b_k^* - a_k^* a_j b_k b_j^*] \\ &= 2 \sum_{j,k} [|a_j|^2 |b_k|^2 - a_j^* a_k b_j b_k^*] \end{aligned}$$

In (3.3) and (3.4) summations are performed with respect to j and to k and the sums are to be taken from 1 to n. On account of its definition as a modulus square $T \geqslant 0$. By (3.3) and (3.4) $T = 2S$. Hence $S \geqslant 0$ so that the inequality (3.2) is proved.

The scalar product of abstract vectors has no simple geometrical meaning. It is nevertheless convenient to call any pair of abstract vectors 'orthogonal' if their scalar product vanishes.

THEOREM (3.A) If a set of vectors is linearly dependent, none of these vectors can be orthogonal to all other vectors of the set.

This is seen as follows:

$$\sum_j c_j \mathbf{a}^{(j)} = 0 \quad c_j \neq 0$$

If $\mathbf{a}^{(k)}$ is a vector out of the set then scalar multiplication by $\mathbf{a}^{(k)}$ results in

$$\sum_{j \neq k} c_j(\mathbf{a}^{(j)}\mathbf{a}^{(k)}) + c_k a_k^2 = 0$$

As the last term cannot vanish there must be at least one non-vanishing scalar product in the sum, thus proving the theorem.

Schmidt's method of orthogonalization

Given a set of linearly independent vectors $\mathbf{a}^{(1)} \ldots \mathbf{a}^{(r)}$ it is possible to derive an equal number of mutually orthogonal vectors $(\mathbf{b}^{(1)} \ldots \mathbf{b}^{(n)})$ by linear combinations of the original vectors. These vectors are determined by the following set of equations

$$\mathbf{b}^{(1)} = \mathbf{a}^{(1)}$$

$$\mathbf{b}^{(2)} = \mathbf{a}^{(2)} - \frac{(\mathbf{b}^{(1)}\mathbf{a}^{(2)})\mathbf{b}^{(1)}}{(b^{(1)})^2} \tag{3.5}$$

$$\mathbf{b}^{(r)} = \mathbf{a}^{(r)} - \frac{(\mathbf{b}^{(j)}\mathbf{a}^{(r)})\mathbf{b}^{(j)}}{(b^{(j)})^2}$$

These formulae are proved by induction. It is assumed that $\mathbf{b}^{(1)} \ldots \mathbf{b}^{(r-1)}$ are mutually orthogonal. On account of this assumption all except two terms of $(\mathbf{b}^{(j)}\mathbf{b}^{(r)})$ vanish. The two non-vanishing terms are $(\mathbf{a}^{(r)}\mathbf{b}^{(j)})$ and

$$\frac{-(\mathbf{a}^{(r)}\mathbf{b}^{(j)})(\mathbf{b}^{(j)}\mathbf{b}^{(j)})}{b_j^2} = -(\mathbf{a}^{(r)}\mathbf{b}^{(j)})$$

Thus the two terms cancel, showing that $\mathbf{b}^{(r)}$ is perpendicular to all $\mathbf{b}^{(j)}$. As $(\mathbf{b}^{(2)}\mathbf{b}^{(1)})$ is seen to be zero the proof is completed.

In this argument no use is made of the linear independence of the vectors $\mathbf{a}^{(j)}$. However, by theorem (3.A) there cannot be any linear dependence of the $\mathbf{b}^{(j)}$. In fact, if the $\mathbf{a}^{(j)}$ are linearly dependent at least one of the $\mathbf{b}^{(j)}$ would be identically zero.

The rules of vector algebra so far, are of limited scope. If it is to be extended it is necessary to define functional relations between vectors other than that of linear combination. That will be achieved in the next chapter.

EXERCISES

1. If complex numbers are regarded as vectors in two dimensions and real numbers as scalars, show that the rules (1.B) and (1.C) apply to complex numbers.

2. Find the components of a vector $\mathbf{x}$ which satisfies the equation

$$2\mathbf{a} - 3\mathbf{x} = \mathbf{b}$$

where $\mathbf{a}$ and $\mathbf{b}$ have the components $(\frac{1}{2}, -1, \frac{3}{2}, -2)$ and $(-2, 1, 0, -1)$ respectively.

3. Show that the vectors $(-1, 0, 1)$; $(0, 1, 1)$; $(1, 1, 0)$ are linearly dependent and that the vectors $(1, 1, 1, 1)$; $(1, i, -1, -i)$, $(i, -i, i, -i)$ are mutually orthogonal.

4. Four vectors in three dimensions are defined as the coefficients of the polynomials

$$\mathbf{f} = 1 + 2x + 3x^2 \qquad \mathbf{g} = -4 + 3x + 3x^2$$
$$\mathbf{h} = 2 - 2x^2 \qquad \mathbf{k} = 4 + 5x - 6x^2$$

Show that they are linearly dependent by proving that

$$-2\mathbf{f} + 48\mathbf{g} + 153\mathbf{h} - 28\mathbf{k} = \mathbf{0}$$

CHAPTER 2

MATRICES

4. Nomenclature

DEFINITION (4.A) A matrix is an ordered array of real or complex numbers aligned in rows and columns so that they form a rectangle, to which are applied certain well-defined rules.

If the number of rows is equal to the number of columns the array is called a square matrix. If the array consists of a single row or a single column it is a row vector or column vector. In this book the term matrix is applied to square matrices only unless any other meaning is explicitly stipulated. A matrix is said to be of nth order or n-dimensional if it consists of n rows and n columns.

A matrix can be specified by writing the array of numbers explicitly and enclosing it in a square bracket as shown below

$$\begin{bmatrix} 5 & -3 & 4+2i \\ 6-i & 0 & 7 \\ 1 & 8i & -9 \end{bmatrix}$$

The numbers of which the matrix is constituted are called matrix elements and can be denoted by a symbol with two subscripts, such as a_{jk}. The first subscript denotes the row, the second the column in which the matrix element stands; j and k are whole numbers ranging from 1 to n in ascending order from left to right and from top to bottom. In the present example $a_{11} = 5$, $a_{12} = -3$, $a_{21} = 6 - i$, $a_{33} = -9$. An alternative notation for matrix elements is $\langle j \mid a \mid k \rangle$ or just $a(j, k)$.

By deleting an equal number of rows and columns of any matrix a 'sub-matrix' of smaller number of rows and columns is defined; in this definition it is understood that the order of the remaining rows and columns is not modified. A single matrix element can be regarded as a one-dimensional sub-matrix.

A matrix can also be regarded as an array of row vectors or of column vectors. They will be denoted by $\mathbf{a}_{j\cdot}$ and $\mathbf{a}_{\cdot k}$ respectively.

Characters like $\mathbf{A}$ will be used to denote the matrix as distinct from matrix elements. In handwritten work it is necessary to denote vectors and matrices in a way which does not depend upon printing techniques. This may be done by underlining symbols for vectors and double underlining symbols for matrices.

Simple matrices may have only two rows and columns, but there is no upper limit for the number of rows and columns. In this book the number of rows and columns will be considered to be finite although the concept of infinite matrices is quite common.

The 'leading diagonal' (or just 'diagonal') of a matrix consists of those elements a_{jk} for which $j = k$. A matrix in which all elements outside the main (i.e. leading) diagonal vanish is called a diagonal matrix. An important special type of diagonal matrix is that in which all diagonal elements are equal to unity. A matrix of this kind is called a unit matrix and denoted by $\mathbf{I}$. Alternatively the notation δ_{jk} ('Kronecker symbol') is in use, implying that it is zero for $j \neq k$ and unity for $j = k$. Matrices in which all elements are zero are called null matrices and conveniently denoted by O.

To every matrix a 'transposed' matrix can be constructed by interchanging rows with columns, the main diagonal remaining unchanged. The transposed matrix to $\mathbf{A}$ is denoted by $\widetilde{\mathbf{A}}$ and $\tilde{a}_{kj} = a_{jk}$. The conjugate complex to the transposed matrix is called the matrix 'adjoint' to $\mathbf{A}$ and is denoted by $\mathbf{A}^{\dagger}$. This term is taken from the adjoint of linear differential operators which are in various respects closely related to matrices. In the mathematical literature the term 'adjoint' is frequently used for 'adjugate', a term to be explained later. Our term 'adjoint' is then replaced by 'Hermitean conjugate'. This nomenclature is unsuitable for our purposes and will not be used in this book. The matrix elements of adjoint matrices are related by

$$a^{\dagger}_{kj} = \tilde{a}^{*}_{jk}$$

The sum of all the diagonal elements of a matrix is called its 'trace'.

The terminology introduced in this section is the basic vocabulary of matrix algebra. It will be used in all arguments to follow.

5. Matrices and vectors

Two matrices are equal if every element of the first is equal to the corresponding element of the second matrix. Thus the equation $\mathbf{A} = \mathbf{B}$ means that $a_{jk} = b_{jk}$ for all values of j and k. A single equation between matrix symbols is a concise expression for n^2 equations between numbers.

The rules for the addition of matrices and the multiplication of matrices by numbers (i.e. scalars) are almost identical with the corresponding rules for vectors.

DEFINITION (5.A) A matrix is multiplied by a scalar by multiplying every single element of the matrix by the scalar. The result is also a matrix of the same size as the original matrix.

DEFINITION (5.B) Two matrices are added by adding their corresponding elements. The result is a matrix. The original matrices *must* be of the same size, however.

On account of the rule for addition the equation $\mathbf{A} = \mathbf{B}$ can be written as $\mathbf{A} - \mathbf{B} = 0$.

It follows from (5.A) and (5.B) that linear combinations of matrices can be formed which are again matrices.

The above rules of matrix algebra will in due course be supplemented by rules for multiplying matrices by other matrices. With these rules mathematical relations between matrices can be established which are to some extent similar to mathematical relations between numbers. This will, however, not be followed up at the present stage because it would be too remote from conventional mathematics and its use in physics. At present it will be shown that relations involving matrices and vectors are closely connected with familiar algebra.

Consider for this purpose the set of simultaneous equations

$$\begin{aligned} a_{11}x_1 + a_{12}x_2 + \ldots + a_{1n}x_n &= y_1 \\ a_{21}x_1 + a_{22}x_2 + \ldots + a_{2n}x_n &= y_2 \\ \vdots \qquad \vdots \qquad\quad \vdots\quad &\quad \vdots \\ a_{n1}x_1 + a_{n2}x_2 + \ldots + a_{nn}x_n &= y_n \end{aligned} \tag{5.1}$$

In these equations the number of terms in each equation on the left-hand side is equal to the number of equations. This need not be so, but we shall not consider simultaneous equations of a more general type here.

Obviously the quantities $x_1 \ldots x_n$ and $y_1 \ldots y_n$ can be regarded as vectors $\mathbf{x}$ and $\mathbf{y}$. $\mathbf{y}$ is obviously a column vector and it is assumed that $\mathbf{x}$ is also a column vector. The coefficients a_{jk} are elements of a matrix $\mathbf{A}$. Equations (5.1) can be written in the compact form

$$\sum_{k=1}^{n} a_{jk}x_k = y_j \quad (j = 1, 2 \ldots n) \tag{5.2}$$

Hence, equations (5.1) can be reduced to a single equation if the multiplication of a column vector by a matrix is defined in accordance with the left-hand side of (5.2).

DEFINITION (5.C) The product of a matrix and a column vector is the column vector $\mathbf{Ax}$ which has the components

$$\sum_k a_{1k}x_k; \quad \sum_k a_{2k}x_k; \ldots \sum_k a_{nk}x_k \tag{5.3}$$

provided that the number of rows in $\mathbf{A}$ is equal to the number of elements in $\mathbf{x}$.

With this definition (5.1) is written as

$$\mathbf{Ax} = \mathbf{y} \tag{5.4}$$

Equation (5.4) can also be expressed in terms of the transposed matrix $\tilde{\mathbf{A}}$. In this case row vectors are required which have the same components as the column vectors $\mathbf{x}$ and $\mathbf{y}$. Then equations (5.2) and (5.4) are written as

$$\sum_j x_j \tilde{a}_{jk} = y_k \tag{5.5}$$

and

$$\tilde{\mathbf{x}}\tilde{\mathbf{A}} = \tilde{\mathbf{y}} \tag{5.6}$$

and the multiplication rule (5.3) is modified in a similar way.

Equation (5.4) shows that a matrix is an operator which transforms any vector into another vector. If a matrix operates on a linear combination of vectors, matrix–vector multiplication commutes with the vector–scalar multiplication and vector addition.

$$\mathbf{A}(\lambda\mathbf{p} + \mu\mathbf{q}) = \lambda(\mathbf{Ap}) + \mu(\mathbf{Aq}) \tag{5.7}$$

On account of this relation matrices are called 'linear operators'.

Equations (5.1) or (5.4) can be interpreted by assuming that $\mathbf{A}$ and $\mathbf{y}$ are given and that the equations have to be solved for the 'unknowns' $x_1 \ldots x_n$ or briefly, for the unknown vector $\mathbf{x}$. In physics equations of similar form occur in various contexts.

If $\mathbf{x}$ and $\mathbf{y}$ are space vectors $\mathbf{A}$ is usually (but not necessarily) a tensor. For example $\mathbf{A}$ could be the dielectric tensor of an anisotropic medium if $\mathbf{x}$ and $\mathbf{y}$ were the electric field strength and the dielectric displacement respectively. In the thermodynamics of irreversible processes the thermodynamic forces and fluxes are regarded as abstract vectors and a matrix, representing the thermodynamic and transport properties of some material, links these vectors by an equation of the type (5.4). The most important application of matrices in classical physics concerns the theory of vibrations; this will be considered in Chapter 8.

EXERCISES

1. Given the matrix

$$\mathbf{A} = \begin{bmatrix} 1+i & 0 & -1 & i \\ 2i & 0 & 2i & 2 \\ -1 & -i & 1 & 4+3i \\ 0 & 1-i & 2 & -2-i \end{bmatrix}$$

express the matrices $\widetilde{\mathbf{A}}$ and $\mathbf{A}^{\dagger}$ in terms of the elements of $\mathbf{A}$. Show that the traces of these matrices vanish.

2. Given the vector $\mathbf{x}$ with the components $(1, -1, i, 1+i)$ calculate $\mathbf{Ax}$, where $\mathbf{A}$ is defined in the preceding exercise.

3. Let the elements of a matrix be time functions. Derive from (5.A), (5.B) and the familiar definition of differential coefficients the differentiation rule for matrices according to which every matrix element is to be differentiated with respect to the time.

4. Given a matrix $\mathbf{A}$ and two vectors $\mathbf{u}$ and $\mathbf{v}$ show that

$$\tilde{\mathbf{v}}^{*}(\mathbf{Au}) = (\tilde{\mathbf{v}}\mathbf{A})^{*}\mathbf{u} \tag{5.8}$$

(Expand both sides of the equation.)

CHAPTER 3

LINEAR EQUATIONS

6. Numerical survey

Problems and questions arising in connection with simultaneous linear equations are conveniently introduced by the way of examples. Consider at first the system of equations

$$\begin{aligned} x_1 + x_2 + x_3 &= 6 \\ x_1 - 2x_2 + 3x_3 &= 2 \\ 2x_1 - 3x_2 + 7x_3 &= 7 \end{aligned} \tag{6.1}$$

It is solved by $x_1 = 3$, $x_2 = 2$, $x_3 = 1$, as conclusively proved by substituting these figures into the equations. The same answer is found by eliminating two of the three unknowns, thus proving that the solution is unique. If the numbers on the right-hand sides are replaced by other numbers the method of elimination is again applicable and yields a unique answer. In particular, if the right-hand sides are 0, 0, 0 the answer is $x_1 = x_2 = x_3 = 0$.

The system

$$\begin{aligned} x_1 + x_2 + x_3 &= 6 \\ x_1 - 2x_2 + 3x_3 &= 2 \\ 3x_1 - 3x_2 + 7x_3 &= 10 \end{aligned} \tag{6.2}$$

is again solved by $x_1 = 3$, $x_2 = 2$, $x_3 = 1$ but now there are alternative solutions such as $x_1 = 13$, $x_2 = -2$, $x_3 = -5$. It is possible to eliminate one of the unknowns but not two of them. If the right-hand sides of (6.2) are replaced by 0, 0, 0 the equations are again solved by $x_1 = x_2 = x_3 = 0$ but there are also non-vanishing solutions; they are not determined uniquely and are merely subject to the condition that $x_2/x_1 = -0{\cdot}4$ and $x_3/x_1 = -0{\cdot}6$. Thus $x_1 = 10$, $x_2 = -4$, $x_3 = -6$ is a solution.

Now let the right-hand side of the third equation of (6.2) be replaced by 8, leaving all the other figures as they are. Eliminating x_2

from the first and second equation and then from the first and third equation two equations for x_1 and x_3 are found.

$$3x_1 + 5x_3 = 14$$
$$3x_1 + 5x_3 = 8$$

They are obviously incompatible; the modified equations do not admit any solution.

These examples show that simultaneous linear equations are not necessarily soluble and that solutions are not necessarily unique.

7. Homogeneous equations

Equations of the form (5.1) or (5.4) are called systems of linear equations. Given the matrix $\mathbf{A}$ and the vector $\mathbf{y}$ they are to be solved for the unknown vector $\mathbf{x}$. It will be assumed that $\mathbf{A}$ is a square matrix, meaning that the number of equations is equal to the number of unknowns. If the vector $\mathbf{y}$ is a null vector the equations are called homogeneous; otherwise they are non-homogeneous. It is attempted to establish conditions for the solubility and the unique solubility of these systems.

In considering the homogeneous equations

$$\mathbf{Ax} = 0 \tag{7.1}$$

it is convenient to express the column vector $\mathbf{x}$ in terms of its components and to regard the matrix as an array of column vectors; thus

$$\mathbf{a}_{\cdot 1}x_1 + \mathbf{a}_{\cdot 2}x_2 + \ldots + \mathbf{a}_{\cdot n}x_n = 0 \tag{7.2}$$

This equation admits the solution $\mathbf{x} = 0$. If equation (7.2) can be solved for non-vanishing $\mathbf{x}$ the existence of that solution establishes a linear dependence of the column vectors, in accordance with the definition (2.A). Thus non-vanishing solutions of homogeneous systems can be defined only if the column vectors of the matrix of coefficients are linearly dependent. Non-vanishing solutions of homogeneous systems cannot be unique. If $\mathbf{x} = \mathbf{u}$ is a solution then $\mathbf{x} = \lambda\mathbf{u}$ is also a solution, λ being any arbitrary scalar. It is sometimes convenient to adjust λ in such a way that $\mathbf{x}$ is 'normalized', meaning that the scalar product of $\mathbf{x}$ with itself is equal to unity.

$$\lambda = [| u_1 |^2 + | u_2 |^2 + \ldots + | u_n |^2]^{-1/2} \tag{7.3}$$

If equation (7.1) is soluble for any $\mathbf{x} \neq 0$ the equation

$$\tilde{\mathbf{x}}\mathbf{A} = 0 \tag{7.4}$$

has also a non-vanishing row vector as a solution. From the solution $\mathbf{x}$ of (7.2) it follows that

$$a_{jn} = -\sum_{k=1}^{n-1} a_{jk}(u_k/u_n) \quad (j = 1 \ldots n) \tag{7.5}$$

It is tacitly assumed that $u_n \neq 0$; this is not essential since u_n and a_{jn} can be replaced by a non-vanishing u_r and a corresponding a_{jr}. The matrix elements

$$a_{j1}, a_{j2} \ldots a_{j(n-1)} \quad (j = 1 \ldots n)$$

are components of $(n-1)$-dimensional vectors. As their number is n, they are, by theorem (2.B), linearly dependent. Thus there exist n numbers $(v_1, v_2 \ldots v_n)$ satisfying the equations

$$\sum_{j=1}^{n} v_j a_{jk} = 0 \quad (k = 1 \ldots (n-1)) \tag{7.6}$$

Also, by (7.5) and (7.6)

$$\sum_{j=1}^{n} v_j a_{jn} = -\sum_{j=1}^{n} v_j \sum_{k=1}^{n-1} a_{jk}(u_k/u_n) \tag{7.7}$$

$$= -\sum_{k=1}^{n-1} (u_k/u_n) \sum_{j=1}^{n} v_j a_{jk} = 0$$

The subscript in equation (7.6) may, accordingly, take all the values $k = 1, 2 \ldots n$. Hence

$$\tilde{\mathbf{v}}\mathbf{A} = 0 \tag{7.8}$$

Thus it is shown that a solution $\tilde{\mathbf{x}} = \tilde{\mathbf{v}}$ of equation (7.4) exists.

Equation (7.8) can be written in terms of the transposed matrix

$$\tilde{\mathbf{A}}\mathbf{v} = 0$$

Thus the columns of the transposed matrix are linearly dependent; as they are identical with the rows of $\mathbf{A}$ and as equation (7.1) can be written as $\tilde{\mathbf{x}}\tilde{\mathbf{A}} = 0$ it is concluded that:

The rows of a matrix are linearly dependent if and only if the columns are linearly dependent.

As homogeneous linear equations play an important part in matrix algebra the results of this section will be frequently referred to.

8. Non-homogeneous equations (i)

The vector equation

$$\mathbf{A}\mathbf{x} = \mathbf{y} \tag{8.1}$$

can be written in a form similar to (7.2) as

$$\mathbf{a}_{\cdot 1}x_1 + \mathbf{a}_{\cdot 2}x_2 + \ldots + \mathbf{a}_{\cdot n}x_n = \mathbf{y} \tag{8.2}$$

As $\mathbf{a}_{\cdot 1}, \mathbf{a}_{\cdot 2} \ldots \mathbf{a}_{\cdot n}, -\mathbf{y}$ are $n+1$ vectors of n components they must be linearly dependent: thus there must be $n+1$ numbers $(q_1 \ldots q_{n+1})$ complying with the equation

$$\mathbf{a}_{\cdot 1}q_1 + \ldots \mathbf{a}_{\cdot n}q_n - \mathbf{y}q_{n+1} = 0$$

If $q_{n+1} \neq 0$ then the numbers $q_1/q_{n+1} \ldots q_n/q_{n+1}$ are the components of a vector $\mathbf{q}'$ and $\mathbf{x} = \mathbf{q}'$ is a solution of (8.1).

It will be at first assumed that the columns of $\mathbf{A}$ are linearly independent. If the component $y_1 \neq 0$ the argument presented in Section 2 can be applied by writing $\mathbf{a}^{(n+1)}$ for $-\mathbf{y}$ and $\mathbf{a}^{(r)}$ for $\mathbf{a}_{.r}$. Then the vectors $\mathbf{b}^{(r)}$ are determined by equation (2.1) and their linear dependence is established as previously. Thus the solubility of equation (8.1) is proved.

If the columns of the matrix $\mathbf{A}$ are linearly independent but $y_1 = 0$ the argument still applies but it is necessary to redefine the vectors $\mathbf{b}^{(r)}$.

Assume that there are two solutions of (8.1) so that $\mathbf{Au} = \mathbf{y}$ and $\mathbf{Au}' = \mathbf{y}$. Then $\mathbf{A}(\mathbf{u} - \mathbf{u}') = 0.(\mathbf{u} - \mathbf{u}')$ is accordingly a solution of the homogeneous equation $\mathbf{Ax} = 0$. Since the columns of $\mathbf{A}$ are assumed to be linearly independent this homogeneous equation has the unique solution $\mathbf{u} - \mathbf{u}' = 0$. Hence any two solutions of (8.1) must be equal to each other; in other words solutions of (8.1) are unique.

This is the type of equation which is usually considered in elementary mathematics.

9. Non-homogeneous equations (ii)

Consider a set of equations of the form (8.1) with different vectors on the right-hand side but with the same matrix. It is again assumed that the column vectors are linearly independent of each other. It is attempted to find the dependence of the unknown vectors on the vector on the right-hand side.

Denoting the right-hand sides of two vector equations by $\mathbf{y}$ and $\mathbf{z}$ and the corresponding solutions by $\mathbf{u}$ and $\mathbf{v}$ respectively, then

$$\mathbf{Au} = \mathbf{y}, \quad \mathbf{Av} = \mathbf{z}$$

and hence

$$\mathbf{A}(\mathbf{u} + \mathbf{v}) = \mathbf{y} + \mathbf{z}$$

Further if the right-hand side is $\lambda\mathbf{y}$ the solution is $\lambda\mathbf{u}$ and if the right-hand side is $\lambda\mathbf{y} + \mu\mathbf{z}$ the solution is $\lambda\mathbf{u} + \mu\mathbf{v}$, λ and μ being any scalar factors. Thus the solution of equations of the type (8.1) can be regarded as a rule by which the unknown vectors are derived from the vectors on the right-hand side. According to the relations listed here this rule corresponds to a linear dependence of a vector upon another vector. It can, accordingly, be represented by a matrix. Hence it should be possible to specify a matrix $\mathbf{B}$ of such a kind that

$$\mathbf{By} = \mathbf{x} \tag{9.1}$$

expresses the solution of equation $\mathbf{A}\mathbf{x} = \mathbf{y}$ in terms of the vector on the right-hand side. In fact, solving equation (8.1) implies finding an expression for the matrix elements of $\mathbf{B}$. The matrix $\mathbf{B}$ must be completely determined by the matrix $\mathbf{A}$, independently of $\mathbf{y}$. Expressions for the matrix $\mathbf{B}$ will be considered later.

It is necessary to consider equation (8.1) on the assumption that the column vectors of $\mathbf{A}$ are linearly dependent. In this case equations $\mathbf{A}\mathbf{x} = 0$ and $\tilde{\mathbf{x}}\mathbf{A} = 0$ have non-vanishing solutions to be denoted by $\mathbf{u}$ and $\tilde{\mathbf{v}}$ respectively. Let $\mathbf{x} = \mathbf{z}$ be a solution of the non-homogeneous equation so that

$$\mathbf{A}\mathbf{z} = \mathbf{y} \tag{9.2}$$

By (5.8) and (7.4)

$$\mathbf{v}^*(\mathbf{A}\mathbf{z}) = (\mathbf{v}\mathbf{A})^*\mathbf{z} = 0$$

so that, by (9.2)

$$(\mathbf{v}^*\mathbf{y}) = 0 \tag{9.3}$$

It follows that simultaneous solubility of the non-homogeneous equations (9.2) and the homogeneous equations (7.4) restricts the admissible vectors $\mathbf{y}$. This restriction is expressed by the equation (9.3) which says that column vectors on the right-hand side of a non-homogeneous equation must be orthogonal to the row vectors which are solutions of one of the homogeneous equations. If that condition is not satisfied non-homogeneous equations are not soluble. If the condition is complied with, the solutions are not unique since, by $\mathbf{A}\mathbf{u} = 0$

$$\mathbf{A}(\mathbf{z} + \mathbf{u}) = \mathbf{y}$$

defines an infinite set of solutions.

In this chapter questions of solubility of linear equations are answered. The numerical or algebraic construction of solutions will not be considered but some general properties of solutions are considered in Chapter 5.

10. 2 x 2 matrices

The study of two-by-two matrices reveals on the one hand the essential features of matrix algebra and is on the other hand free of unnecessary complications. For this reason two-by-two matrices are considered in greater detail both in this section and later.

As these matrices have four elements it will be attempted to represent them as linear combinations of four 'basic' matrices. Selection of these matrices is somewhat arbitrary, but the unit matrix is an obvious first choice. In addition three matrices are adopted which are applied in various fields of theoretical physics. The basic matrices are

$$\mathbf{I} = \begin{bmatrix} 1 & 0 \\ 0 & 1 \end{bmatrix} \quad \mathbf{X} = \begin{bmatrix} 0 & \mathrm{i} \\ -\mathrm{i} & 0 \end{bmatrix} \quad \mathbf{Y} = \begin{bmatrix} 0 & 1 \\ 1 & 0 \end{bmatrix} \quad \mathbf{Z} = \begin{bmatrix} -1 & 0 \\ 0 & 1 \end{bmatrix} \tag{10.1}$$

$\mathbf{X}$, $\mathbf{Y}$, and $\mathbf{Z}$ are known as 'spin matrices'. Every matrix in two dimensions can be written as

$$\mathbf{A} = p\mathbf{I} + q\mathbf{X} + r\mathbf{Y} + s\mathbf{Z} \tag{10.2}$$

where p, q, r, s are numbers.

In order to apply (10.2) it is necessary to determine p, q, r and s in accordance with the simultaneous equations

$$\begin{aligned} p - s &= a_{11} & \qquad -\mathrm{i}q + r &= a_{21} \\ \mathrm{i}q + r &= a_{12} & p + s &= a_{22} \end{aligned}$$

It follows that

$$\begin{aligned} p &= \tfrac{1}{2}(a_{22} + a_{11}) & \qquad s &= \tfrac{1}{2}(a_{22} - a_{11}) \\ r &= \tfrac{1}{2}(a_{12} + a_{21}) & q &= -\tfrac{1}{2}\mathrm{i}(a_{12} - a_{21}) \end{aligned} \tag{10.3}$$

Consider now an important function of matrix elements which is called the determinant of the matrix. It will first be discussed in connection with 2×2 matrices.

The determinant is defined as

$$\det \mathbf{A} = \begin{vmatrix} a_{11} & a_{12} \\ a_{21} & a_{22} \end{vmatrix} = a_{11}a_{22} - a_{12}a_{21} \tag{10.4}$$

Important properties of determinants can be verified by the use of equation (10.4), for example

$$\begin{vmatrix} 1 & 0 \\ 0 & 1 \end{vmatrix} = 1 \tag{10.5}$$

$$\begin{vmatrix} \lambda a_{11} & a_{12} \\ \lambda a_{21} & a_{22} \end{vmatrix} = \lambda \begin{vmatrix} a_{11} & a_{12} \\ a_{21} & a_{22} \end{vmatrix} \tag{10.6}$$

$$\begin{vmatrix} (a_{11} + a_{12}) & a_{12} \\ (a_{21} + a_{22}) & a_{22} \end{vmatrix} = \begin{vmatrix} a_{11} & a_{12} \\ a_{21} & a_{22} \end{vmatrix} \tag{10.7}$$

Equation (10.7) shows that determinants of different matrices may be equal to each other.

The concept of determinants would have to be regarded as artificial and abstruse were it not for their relations to the solution of linear equations. Consider the system

$$\begin{aligned} a_{11}x_1 + a_{12}x_2 &= y_1 \\ a_{21}x_1 + a_{22}x_2 &= y_2 \end{aligned} \tag{10.8}$$

and assume that it admits a unique solution. Multiplying the first equation by a_{22}, the second by a_{21} and then subtracting eliminates x_2, yielding an equation for x_1:

$$(a_{11}a_{22} - a_{12}a_{21})x_1 = y_1a_{22} - y_2a_{12} \tag{10.9}$$

Multiplying the first equation by a_{21}, the second by a_{11} and then subtracting eliminates x_1 and yields an equation for x_2:

$$(a_{12}a_{21} - a_{11}a_{22})x_2 = y_1a_{21} - y_2a_{11} \tag{10.10}$$

Equations (10.9) and (10.10) can be written, and accordingly solved, in terms of determinants:

$$\begin{aligned} x_1 \begin{vmatrix} a_{11} & a_{12} \\ a_{21} & a_{22} \end{vmatrix} &= \begin{vmatrix} y_1 & a_{12} \\ y_2 & a_{22} \end{vmatrix} \\ x_2 \begin{vmatrix} a_{11} & a_{12} \\ a_{21} & a_{22} \end{vmatrix} &= \begin{vmatrix} a_{11} & y_1 \\ a_{21} & y_2 \end{vmatrix} \end{aligned} \tag{10.11}$$

From these examples it emerges that determinants may be important with respect to the solution of simultaneous equations. For this reason in the following chapter determinants of general matrices are considered.

EXERCISES

1. Given the matrix

$$\mathbf{A} = \begin{bmatrix} 2 & 1 & -3 \\ 3 & -4 & 2 \\ -5 & 3 & 1 \end{bmatrix}$$

and the vector $\mathbf{y}$ having the components -5, 1, 4 show that the equation $\mathbf{Ax} = \mathbf{y}$ is solved by the vector (1, 2, 3) and also by the vector (11, 15, 14). Hence derive a solution of the equation $\mathbf{Ax} = 0$.

2. Derive the traces and determinants of the matrices (10.1).

3. Solve by elimination

$$\begin{aligned} 5x_1 + 3x_2 &= 1 \\ 2x_1 - 4x_2 &= -1 \end{aligned}$$

Show that this agrees with the solution obtained by applying equation (10.11).

CHAPTER 4

DETERMINANTS

11. Definition and properties

The determinant of a 3×3 matrix $\mathbf{D}$ is defined as

$$\begin{aligned}\det \mathbf{D} = {} & d_{11}d_{22}d_{33} + d_{12}d_{23}d_{31} \\ & + d_{13}d_{21}d_{32} - d_{11}d_{23}d_{32} - d_{12}d_{21}d_{33} \\ & - d_{13}d_{22}d_{31}\end{aligned}$$

These expressions are related to equations with three unknowns in a way comparable to (10.11) but the necessary deductions are cumbersome. For matrices of 4th or higher order any direct definition is hard to appreciate and even harder to evaluate. For this reason the general definition of determinants will be given implicitly in terms of their most important properties and from this indirect definition all those relations can be derived which will be required later.

DEFINITION (11.A) A determinant of nth order is a scalar function of an $n \times n$ matrix, specified in terms of column vectors and subject to three conditions:

(α) The determinant of any unit matrix is equal to unity.
(β) If a matrix $\mathbf{B}$ is derived from a matrix $\mathbf{A}$ by multiplying a column vector by a scalar factor λ then $\det \mathbf{B} = \lambda \det \mathbf{A}$.
(γ) If a matrix $\mathbf{C}$ is derived from a matrix $\mathbf{A}$ by adding a column vector to another column vector then $\det \mathbf{C} = \det \mathbf{A}$.

These definitions are generalizations of equations (10.5), (10.6) and (10.7).

Other properties of determinants are readily derived from the definition.

THEOREM (11.B) If a matrix $\mathbf{B}$ is derived from a matrix $\mathbf{A}$ by adding a scalar multiple of a column vector to another column vector then $\det \mathbf{B} = \det \mathbf{A}$.

By (β) det $\mathbf{A}$ becomes λ det $\mathbf{A}$ if the column vector $\mathbf{a}_{.s}$ is multiplied by λ. This value persists if $\lambda\mathbf{a}_{.s}$ is added to $\mathbf{a}_{.r}$ on account of (γ). Subsequent multiplication of $\lambda\mathbf{a}_{.s}$ by $1/\lambda$ reduces the column vector and the determinant to their original values, whereas the vector $\mathbf{a}_{.r}$ has been replaced by $\mathbf{a}_{.r} + \lambda\mathbf{a}_{.s}$.

THEOREM (11.C) If two columns of the matrix $\mathbf{A}$ are permuted, the determinant of the resulting matrix $\mathbf{D}$ is det $\mathbf{D} = -$ det $\mathbf{A}$.

From $\mathbf{A}$ new matrices are derived by successive substitutions.

$$\begin{aligned} \mathbf{a}'_{.r} &= \mathbf{a}_{.r} + \mathbf{a}_{.s} & \mathbf{a}'_{.s} &= \mathbf{a}_{.s} \\ \mathbf{a}''_{.r} &= \mathbf{a}'_{.r} & \mathbf{a}''_{.s} &= \mathbf{a}'_{.s} - \mathbf{a}'_{.r} = -\mathbf{a}_{.r} \\ \mathbf{a}'''_{.r} &= \mathbf{a}''_{.r} + \mathbf{a}''_{.s} = \mathbf{a}_{.s} & \mathbf{a}'''_{.s} &= \mathbf{a}''_{.s} = -\mathbf{a}_{.r} \end{aligned}$$

By (γ) the determinants of the resulting matrices are equal to det $\mathbf{A}$ whereas the column $\mathbf{a}_{.r}$ is replaced by $\mathbf{a}_{.s}$ and the column $\mathbf{a}_{.s}$ is replaced by $-\mathbf{a}_{.r}$. Subsequent multiplication of column $\mathbf{a}'''_{.s}$ by (-1) completes the permutation of the columns and multiplies the determinant by (-1).

THEOREM (11.D) If any column in a matrix is a null vector the determinant is zero.

Multiplication of any column by the scalar factor $\lambda \neq 0$ must, in accordance with (β) multiply the determinant by λ. Multiplication of the null vector by λ does not change the column and, accordingly, could not change the determinant. These two statements are incompatible unless the determinant vanishes.

12. Evaluation of determinants

In spite of its indirect approach the definition (11.A) can be used for deriving the numerical value of determinants.

THEOREM (12.A) The determinant of a diagonal matrix is equal to the product of the diagonal elements.

Beginning with a unit matrix which has the determinant unity, the column vectors and hence the diagonal elements are successively multiplied by $a_{11} \ldots a_{nn}$, the diagonal elements of the diagonal matrix $\mathbf{A}$. Hence the proposition is proved.

Consider now a matrix

$$\mathbf{B} = \begin{bmatrix} b_{11} & 0 & 0 \ldots 0 \\ b_{21} & b_{22} & 0 \ldots 0 \\ b_{31} & b_{32} & b_{33} \ldots 0 \\ \\ b_{n1} & b_{n2} & b_{n3} \ldots b_{nn} \end{bmatrix} \tag{12.1}$$

in which all elements to the right of the diagonal are zero ($b_{jk} = 0$ for $k > j$).

In order to find the determinant of **B** the last column is multiplied by $(-b_{n1}/b_{nn})$ and added to the first column thus replacing b_{n1} by 0 without affecting any other matrix element. By a similar procedure the elements $b_{n2}, b_{n3} \ldots b_{n(n-1)}$ can be replaced by 0 without any other matrix element being changed. In the same way, all terms in the $(n-1)$th row left of the leading diagonal are replaced by 0 and eventually all matrix elements to the left of the diagonal are made to vanish without changing the diagonal elements. The determinant is not affected by these substitutions; it must accordingly be equal to the determinant of the diagonal matrix to which **B** is finally converted. This determinant is equal to the product of the diagonal elements of the diagonal matrix and, accordingly, to the product of the diagonal elements of **B** itself.

Thus it is possible to evaluate the determinant of any matrix which can be converted to the form (12.1) by linear combination of columns. For this purpose the matrix $\mathbf{A}^{(1)}$ is in succession converted to $\mathbf{A}^{(2)}$, $\mathbf{A}^{(3)} \ldots \mathbf{B}$ by the substitutions

$$\begin{aligned} a_{jk}^{(2)} &= a_{jk}^{(1)} - \left[\frac{a_{j1}^{(1)} a_{1k}^{(1)}}{a_{11}^{(1)}}\right] \quad (k = 2 \ldots n) \\ a_{jk}^{(3)} &= a_{jk}^{(2)} - \left[\frac{a_{j2}^{(2)} a_{2k}^{(2)}}{a_{22}^{(2)}}\right] \quad (k = 3 \ldots n) \qquad (12.2) \\ b_{jk} &= a_{jk}^{(n-1)} - \left[\frac{a_{j(n-1)}^{(n-1)} a_{(n-1)k}^{(n-1)}}{a_{(n-1)(n-1)}^{(n-1)}}\right] \quad (k = n) \end{aligned}$$

Before performing any of these substitutions it is necessary to make sure that the diagonal element in the denominator does not vanish. If it is zero, the substitution is preceded by a permutation or a linear combination of columns in order to replace the zero in the diagonal element. If any of the columns is converted to a null vector the value of the determinant is identified as zero. By this method the determinant of every matrix is uniquely defined.

Matrix elements of $\mathbf{A}^{(r)}$ depend on the elements of $\mathbf{A}^{(r-1)}$ in the columns $k \geqslant r$ and $j \geqslant r$. Expressions for $a_{jk}^{(r)}$ and $a_{kj}^{(r)}$ depend on the elements of $\mathbf{A}^{(r-1)}$ in such a way that they are converted into each other by permuting j and k. This remains true if they are expressed in terms of the elements of $\mathbf{A}^{(r-2)} \ldots \mathbf{A}^{(1)}$. Diagonal elements of $\mathbf{A}^{(r)}$ and, in particular, of **B** depend on the rows and columns of $\mathbf{A}^{(1)}$ in an entirely symmetric way. As the determinant of $\mathbf{A}^{(1)}$ depends on the diagonal elements b_{jj} only it is not changed by transposing:

$$\det \widetilde{\mathbf{A}} = \det \mathbf{A} \qquad (12.3)$$

For the same reason the term 'column' can be replaced by 'row' in

(11.A), (11.B), and (11.C) and in the results to follow whenever properties of determinants are considered.

13. Expansion of determinants

The way in which determinants depend upon the matrix elements is conveniently studied by the way of an expansion

$$\det \mathbf{A} = a_{11}\alpha_{11} + a_{12}\alpha_{12} + \ldots + a_{1n}\alpha_{1n} \tag{13.1}$$

the validity of which is to be established in this section. The coefficients α_{1k} are called the cofactors of a_{1k} and depend upon matrix elements outside the first row and the kth column. By deleting $\mathbf{a}_{1\cdot}$ and $\mathbf{a}_{\cdot k}$ a matrix with one row and column less than $\mathbf{A}$ is defined. The determinant of this matrix multiplied by $(-1)^{1+k}$ is the cofactor of a_{1k}. The expansion (13.1) can, on account of the symmetric dependence of determinants on rows and columns be converted to an expansion progressing in elements of the first column.

Consider at first a matrix the last column of which consists of variables $a_{jn} = x_j$ whereas the other matrix elements are fixed numbers. If the substitutions (12.2) are performed the variables x_j are grouped into homogeneous linear functions in which every term carries a factor x_j. If all matrix elements to the right of the diagonal are replaced by zero the variables x_j are assembled in the matrix elements b_{kk} whereas all other matrix elements are independent of the variables. The determinant is, accordingly, a linear function of $x_1 \ldots x_n$. Thus determinants are linear functions of the elements in the last column. However any column can be interchanged with any other column of the determinant without affecting the value of the determinant, but changing its sign. The following theorem is therefore proved.

THEOREM (13.A) Determinants are linear homogeneous functions of the matrix elements.

It follows that a determinant can be expanded as follows:

$$\det \mathbf{A} = a_{11}q_1 + a_{12}q_2 + \ldots + a_{1n}q_n$$

where the coefficients are independent of the matrix elements of the first row.

In order to identify the factor q_1 consider a matrix $\mathbf{A}^{(1)}$ in which the first row of $\mathbf{A}$ is replaced by $(1\ 0\ 0 \ldots 0)$. This is converted by the substitution

$$a_{jk}^{(2)} = a_{jk}^{(1)} - \left[\frac{a_{j1}^{(1)}a_{1k}^{(1)}}{a_{11}^{(1)}}\right]$$

into a matrix in which the elements of the first row and the first column vanish, excepting $a_{11}^{(2)} = 1$. The sub-matrix which remains after deleting the first row and the first column involves those matrix elements upon which q_1 depends. Now

$$\det \mathbf{A}^{(1)} = \det \mathbf{A}^{(2)} = q_1$$

q_1 remains accordingly unchanged if one column is added to another out of the columns 2 to n. Also if any of these column vectors is multiplied by any scalar factor, q_1 is multiplied by this scalar. q_1 would be equal to unity if the matrix $\mathbf{A}^{(2)}$ and, accordingly, the sub-matrix, were a unit matrix. It follows then that q_1 as a function of the matrix elements of the sub-matrix must be a determinant; since this function is uniquely defined q_1 must be equal to α_{11}.

In identifying the factors $q_2, q_3 \ldots q_n$ the first row of $\mathbf{A}$ is successively replaced by a row in which the 2nd, 3rd ... nth element is equal to 1, the other elements being equal to 0. The second column is permuted with the first column and the above argument is repeated; remembering that the permutation changes the sign of the determinant, q_2 is identified as α_{12}. The third column is permuted with the second thus involving another change of sign and allowing q_3 to be identified with α_{13}. Continuing in this manner, all factors q_k are seen to be equal to the cofactors.

After having established the validity of the expansion (13.1) this same expansion can be applied to the cofactors. It is not necessary to present any expansion formulae explicitly. It is sufficient to notice that by continued application of the series (13.1) every determinant can be derived from determinants of 2nd order which are explicitly defined in Section 10.

If in equation (13.1) the matrix elements a_{1k} are replaced by a_{2k} the series is equal to the determinant of a matrix in which the first row is equal to the second row and which vanishes accordingly. The same is true if in (13.1) the first row is replaced by any other row:

$$a_{j1}\alpha_{11} + a_{j2}\alpha_{12} + \ldots + a_{jn}\alpha_{1n} = 0 \quad (j = 2, 3 \ldots n) \quad (13.2)$$

14. Proof of consistency

This section is only indirectly linked to the other parts of the book. It is added for the benefit of those readers who insist on rigour in mathematical deductions.

The arguments of Sections 11–13 are established on the tacit assumption that the conditions (α), (β), and (γ) of (11.A) are mutually compatible. This is not self-evident; construction of determinants by applying the expansion (13.1) could fail.

It will now be shown that the validity of the three conditions of matrices of order $n - 1$ implies their validity for matrices of nth order. Their validity for 2×2 matrices has been demonstrated in Section 10.

The existence of $(n - 1)$th order determinants is assumed and it is shown that the right-hand side of (13.1) complies with the three conditions (11.A).

Inspection of equation (13.1) shows that condition (β) is complied with: any scalar multiplier of the row $\mathbf{a}_{1\cdot}$ multiplies det $\mathbf{A}$. Every scalar multiplier of any other row multiplies the cofactors and hence det $\mathbf{A}$. If $\mathbf{A}$ is a unit matrix, a_{11} and α_{11} are equal to unity and the other terms in the series vanish. Hence condition (α) is complied with. Validity of condition (γ) is obvious as far as rows 2 to n are concerned, since these rows belong to the cofactors. It remains to prove that addition of the first row to the second or of the second row to the first does not change the determinant; if this proof is successful it also applies to addition of the first row to all rows from 3 to n.

Expanding the cofactors α_{1k} in the elements of the second row

$$\det \mathbf{A} = \sum_j \sum_k a_{1j} a_{2k} \beta_{jk} \tag{14.1}$$

where the coefficients are independent of the elements in the first and second row. $\pm\beta_{jk}$ is equal to the determinant of the matrix derived from $\mathbf{A}$ by deleting rows 1 and 2 and columns j and k. $\beta_{jj} = 0$ since the cofactor of a_{1j} is independent of the column j; β_{rs} and β_{sr} differ, if at all, only by their sign. Thus (14.1) can be written as

$$\det \mathbf{A} = \sum_{j=2}^{n} \sum_{k=1}^{j-1} \beta_{jk} a_{1j} a_{2k} + \sum_{j=2}^{n} \sum_{k=j+1}^{n} \beta_{jk} a_{1j} a_{2k} + a_{11} \sum_{k=2}^{n} \beta_{1k} a_{2k} \tag{14.2}$$

Counting the number of columns in the cofactors from the lowest to the kth inclusive, one finds in the first term of (14.2) k columns, in the second term $k - 1$ columns, in the third term $k - 2$ columns. As the sign of the cofactors is $(-1)^{1+j}$, the sign of β_{jk} is $(-1)^{1+j+k}$ in the first term, $(-1)^{j+k}$ in the second term and $(-1)^{j+k-1}$ in the third term. Hence $\beta_{rs} = -\beta_{sr}$ and (14.1) can be written as

$$\det \mathbf{A} = \sum_{r=2}^{n} \sum_{s=1}^{n-1} \beta_{rs}(a_{1r} a_{2s} - a_{1s} a_{2r}) \tag{14.3}$$

This expression is not changed if the first or the second row—but not both simultaneously—are replaced by the sum of the two rows.

This result completes the induction proof; the compatibility of the conditions (11.A) and the existence of determinants of every order is thus proved.

EXERCISES

1. Evaluate the determinants

$$\begin{vmatrix} 4 & 2 & 1 \\ 3 & 2 & 2 \\ 1 & 4 & 3 \end{vmatrix} \quad \text{and} \quad \begin{vmatrix} -3 & -2 & 2 & 3 \\ 1 & -1 & -1 & 1 \\ 2 & 1 & 0 & 2 \\ 3 & -1 & 1 & -3 \end{vmatrix}$$

2. Show that the matrix

$$\begin{bmatrix} 2 & 3+4i & 5i \\ 3-4i & 3 & 1 \\ -5i & 1 & -1 \end{bmatrix}$$

has a real determinant.

3. Using the theorems of Section 11, show that the determinant of a matrix must vanish if two rows are equal to each other.

4. Using the definition of cofactors, the expansion (13.1), equation (12.3) and theorem (11.C) show that the expansion

$$\det \mathbf{A} = \sum_{k=1}^{n} a_{jk}\alpha_{jk}$$

is valid and hence that

$$\sum_{j=1}^{n} a_{jk}\alpha_{jm} = \delta_{jm} \det \mathbf{A}$$

5. Show that repeated substitutions of the form (12.2) convert the matrix

$$\mathbf{A} = \begin{bmatrix} -1 & 1 & 1 & 1 \\ 1 & 1 & 1 & -1 \\ 1 & 1 & -1 & 1 \\ 1 & -1 & 1 & 1 \end{bmatrix}$$

to

$$\mathbf{B} = \begin{bmatrix} -1 & 0 & 0 & 0 \\ 1 & 2 & 0 & 0 \\ 1 & 2 & -2 & 0 \\ 1 & 0 & 2 & 4 \end{bmatrix}$$

and thus derive $\det \mathbf{A}$. (The matrix obtained by permuting the 2nd and 4th column of $\mathbf{A}$ would yield after the first substitution a vanishing diagonal element although the determinant does not vanish.)

CHAPTER 5

MATRICES AND LINEAR EQUATIONS

15. Determinants and homogeneous equations

Consider a matrix **A** with columns which are linearly dependent. In this case

$$\sum_{r} \mathbf{a}_{\cdot r} x_r = 0$$

not all x_r being zero; if in addition $x_1 \neq 0$

$$\mathbf{a}_{\cdot 1} = -\sum_{r=2}^{n} \mathbf{a}_{\cdot r}(x_r/x_1)$$

By successive addition of all $\mathbf{a}_{\cdot r}(x_r/x_1)$ to the vector $\mathbf{a}_{\cdot 1}$, this vector is converted to a null vector so that the determinant vanishes. If $x_1 = 0$ this can be proved after a permutation of columns.

THEOREM (15.A) If the column vectors of a matrix are linearly dependent the determinant of the matrix vanishes.

On account of the argument in Section 7 the term 'row vectors' may be substituted for 'column vectors' in (15.A). The inverse of theorem (15.A) says:

THEOREM (15.B) If the determinant of a matrix vanishes, the columns are linearly dependent.

Consider an $(n \times n)$ matrix **B** with columns that are linearly independent. By permutation of columns it is then possible to make $a_{11} \neq 0$. By a substitution of the form (12.2) the elements $b_{12} \ldots b_{1n}$ are replaced by 0. The sub-matrix derived from **B** by deleting the first row and column must have linearly independent columns. For if, for non-vanishing q,

$$\sum_{k=2}^{n} b_{jk} q_k = 0 \quad (j = 2 \ldots n)$$

it would be possible to choose $q_1 = 0$ and to establish the linear dependence

$$\sum_{k=1}^{n} b_{jk} q_k = 0$$

contrary to premises.

In the present instance

$$\det \mathbf{B} = b_{11}\beta_{11}$$

β_{11} being the cofactor to b_{11}. If it is assumed that it has been proved (15.B) is valid for $(n-1) \times (n-1)$ matrices this cofactor is non-zero. As $b_{11} \neq 0$ this would show that $\det \mathbf{B} \neq 0$. Thus validity of theorem (15.B) for matrices of any order would imply the validity of theorem (15.B) for matrices of the next higher order. Thus it remains to show that it is valid for 2×2 matrices.

Assuming that the determinant vanishes,

$$a_{11}a_{22} - a_{12}a_{21} = 0$$

it follows that

$$(a_{11}/a_{21}) = (a_{12}/a_{22}) = \gamma$$

Then the matrix has the form

$$\begin{bmatrix} \gamma a_{21} & \gamma a_{22} \\ a_{21} & a_{22} \end{bmatrix}$$

So that the linear dependence is established

$$\mathbf{a}_{1\cdot} - \gamma \mathbf{a}_{2\cdot} = 0$$

Theorem (15.B) is accordingly true for second-order matrices, and, on account of the above induction, for matrices of every higher order.

On account of the results of Section 7 one arrives at the following general conclusion.

THEOREM (15.C) A homogeneous system of linear equations

$$\mathbf{A}\mathbf{x} = 0$$

admits solutions $\mathbf{x} \neq 0$ if and only if $\det \mathbf{A} = 0$.

From this theorem the most important deductions in matrix algebra are derived.

16. Products and powers of matrices

Multiplication of a vector by a matrix generates another vector. This vector may be multiplied again by a matrix. Thus if

$$\mathbf{B}\mathbf{u} = \mathbf{v} \quad \text{and} \quad \mathbf{A}\mathbf{v} = \mathbf{w}$$

the resulting equation

$$\mathbf{A}\mathbf{B}\mathbf{u} = \mathbf{w}$$

says that the 'product matrix' **AB** multiplies the vector **u** and generates the vector **w**. In terms of components this comes to

$$\sum_j b_{kj}u_j = v_k \qquad \sum_k a_{mk}v_k = w_m$$

$$\sum_k \sum_j a_{mk}b_{kj}u_j = w_m$$

Hence the matrix element of the product matrix **C** = **AB** is given by

$$c_{mk} = \sum_j a_{mj}b_{jk} \tag{16.1}$$

The subscript j is a 'dummy' and does not enter in the result. Equation (16.1) is an expression for the rule of matrix multiplication.

As the multiplication of vectors by matrices can be repeated any number of times and its result is unambiguous, matrix multiplication should comply with the associative law

$$\mathbf{A}(\mathbf{BC}) = (\mathbf{AB})\mathbf{C} \tag{16.2}$$

This is verified by applying equation (16.1). Matrix elements of **BC** are given by

$$\sum_m b_{km}c_{mp}$$

so that the left-hand side of (16.2) is

$$\sum_k a_{jk} \sum_m b_{km}c_{mp} \tag{16.3}$$

The matrix elements of **AB** are given by

$$\sum_k a_{jk}b_{km}$$

so that the right-hand side of (16.2) is

$$\sum_k a_{jk} \sum_m b_{km}c_{mp} \tag{16.4}$$

Since all summation signs can be shifted to the left of the matrix expressions (16.3) and (16.4) are equal to each other and conveniently written as

$$\sum_k \sum_m a_{jk}b_{km}c_{mp}$$

thus proving the associative law.

The commutative law of multiplication does not apply to matrices. The products **AB** and **BA** need not be equal to each other. If in a particular instance the two products are equal the matrices **A** and **B** are said to 'commute'. Every matrix commutes with the unit matrix:

$$\mathbf{AI} = \mathbf{IA} = \mathbf{A} \tag{16.5}$$

Powers of matrices are explained in terms of repeated multiplication. $\mathbf{A}^2$ has the elements $\Sigma_k a_{jk}a_{km}$ and $\mathbf{A}^3 = \mathbf{A}^2\mathbf{A} = \mathbf{A}\mathbf{A}^2$.

The product of two matrices may be the null matrix even if both factors differ from zero. This is an important difference between the algebra of numbers and of matrices but it is not of great importance in the applications to physics given in this book.

By the rules of addition and multiplication matrix polynomials are defined which behave in many respects like polynomials of numbers. Thus

$$\mathbf{P} = 5\mathbf{I} + 4\mathbf{A} - 3\mathbf{A}^2 + 2\mathbf{A}^3$$

is a matrix with the elements

$$p_{jm} = 5\delta_{jm} + 4a_{jm} - 3\sum_k a_{jk}a_{km} + 2\sum_m \sum_l a_{jk}a_{kl}a_{lm}$$

If the necessary conditions of convergence are complied with, it is possible to define transcendental functions of matrices by way of infinite series, for instance

$$e^{\mathbf{A}} = \mathbf{I} + \sum_{n=1}^{\infty} (1/n!)\mathbf{A}^n$$

However, if $\mathbf{A}$ and $\mathbf{B}$ do not commute, then $e^{\mathbf{A}}\, e^{\mathbf{B}}$ is not equal to $e^{\mathbf{A}+\mathbf{B}}$.

From $\mathbf{C} = \mathbf{AB}$ it follows that

$$\tilde{c}_{jm} = c_{mj} = \sum_k a_{mk}b_{kj} = \sum_k a_{km}b_{jk}$$
$$= \sum_k b_{jk}a_{km}$$

Hence $$\tilde{\mathbf{C}} = \tilde{\mathbf{B}}\tilde{\mathbf{A}} \qquad (16.6)$$

In a similar way it can be shown that the adjoint of a matrix product is equal to the product of the adjoint matrices taken in the inverse order

$$(\mathbf{AB})^\dagger = \mathbf{B}^\dagger\mathbf{A}^\dagger \qquad (16.7)$$

At this stage the question arises whether a division of a matrix by another matrix can be defined. Given a matrix $\mathbf{A}$ it might be possible to identify another matrix $\mathbf{B}$ which complies with the condition $\mathbf{BA} = \mathbf{I}$. If this matrix exists it would conveniently be denoted by $\mathbf{A}^{-1}$ and called the reciprocal (or inverse) of $\mathbf{A}$. If $\mathbf{B}$ also has a reciprocal then

$$\mathbf{B}^{-1}\mathbf{BAB} = \mathbf{B}^{-1}\mathbf{B} = \mathbf{I}$$

and hence $\mathbf{AB} = \mathbf{I}$ so that there is a pair of mutually reciprocal and commuting matrices. In this way negative powers of matrices are defined.

Assuming that matrices $\mathbf{B}$ and $\mathbf{C}$ are given and $\mathbf{B}$ has a reciprocal then division of $\mathbf{C}$ by $\mathbf{B}$ would have a meaning because $\mathbf{X} = \mathbf{CB}^{-1}$ would satisfy the equation $\mathbf{XB} = \mathbf{C}$.

The reciprocal of a matrix product is given by

$$(\mathbf{AB})^{-1} = \mathbf{B}^{-1}\mathbf{A}^{-1} \tag{16.8}$$

This follows from

$$(\mathbf{B}^{-1}\mathbf{A}^{-1})(\mathbf{AB}) = \mathbf{B}^{-1}\mathbf{IB} = \mathbf{B}^{-1}\mathbf{B} = \mathbf{I}$$

Apart from the rule (16.1) a different kind of multiplication of matrices has been defined and is occasionally used.

Given a $\nu \times \nu$ matrix $\mathbf{P}$ and a $\mu \times \mu$ matrix $\mathbf{Q}$ the 'direct product' of these matrices is defined as an $\nu\mu \times \nu\mu$ matrix $\mathbf{R}$

$$\mathbf{R} = \mathbf{P} \times \mathbf{Q}$$

Every element of $\mathbf{R}$ is the product of an element of $\mathbf{P}$ and an element of $\mathbf{Q}$. $\mathbf{R}$ consists of sub-matrices in which every element of $\mathbf{P}$ appears in the right order and is multiplied into one and the same element of $\mathbf{Q}$. In general $\mathbf{Q} \times \mathbf{P}$ differs from $\mathbf{P} \times \mathbf{Q}$.

However, ordinary multiplication and direct multiplication commute. If $\mathbf{P}$ and $\mathbf{S}$ are $\nu \times \nu$ matrices and $\mathbf{Q}$ and $\mathbf{T}$ are $\mu \times \mu$ matrices and $\mathbf{R} = \mathbf{P} \times \mathbf{Q}$, $\mathbf{U} = \mathbf{S} \times \mathbf{T}$ then

$$\mathbf{RU} = (\mathbf{P} \times \mathbf{Q})(\mathbf{S} \times \mathbf{T}) = \mathbf{PS} \times \mathbf{QT} \tag{16.9}$$

This is proved by evaluation of the product in terms of matrix elements. As the proof is lengthy, but otherwise trivial, it is omitted. It may be noticed that the direct product of diagonal matrices is a diagonal matrix.

17. Equations admitting unique solutions

Consider an equation

$$\mathbf{A}\mathrm{x} = \mathrm{y} \tag{17.1}$$

and let the columns of $\mathbf{A}$ be linearly independent. According to Sections 8 and 9 equation (17.1) is uniquely soluble and the solution can be given in the form

$$\mathrm{x} = \mathbf{B}\mathrm{y} \tag{17.2}$$

where the matrix $\mathbf{B}$ is independent of the vector y. Equations (17.1) and (17.2) imply that

$$\mathbf{BA}\mathrm{x} = \mathbf{B}\mathrm{y} = \mathrm{x}$$
$$\mathbf{AB}\mathrm{y} = \mathbf{A}\mathrm{x} = \mathrm{y}$$

and hence that

$$\mathbf{AB} = \mathbf{BA} = \mathbf{I}$$

The matrix **B** is, accordingly, the reciprocal of **A**. If the determinant of a matrix differs from 0 the matrix has certainly a reciprocal.

If det $\mathbf{A} = 0$ then the equation $\mathbf{Ax} = 0$ is soluble for $x \neq 0$. Then $\mathbf{BAx} = 0$ for any matrix **B**. If **B** were the reciprocal of **A** then $\mathbf{BAx} = \mathbf{Ix} = 0$ with $x \neq 0$. This is impossible. It follows that **A** cannot have a reciprocal.

THEOREM (17.A) A matrix has a reciprocal if and only if its determinant does not vanish.

This theorem is analogous to the exclusion of division by 0 in the algebra of numbers.

The elements of the reciprocal matrix of **A** are determined by the equations

$$\sum_k a_{jk} a_{km}^{-1} = \delta_{jm}$$

which can be solved by comparison with the expansion

$$\sum_k a_{jk} \alpha_{mk} = (\det \mathbf{A}) \delta_{jm}$$

so that

$$a_{km}^{-1} = (\det \mathbf{A})^{-1} \tilde{\alpha}_{km} \tag{17.3}$$

The matrix $\mathbf{A}^{-1}(\det \mathbf{A})$ is called the 'adjugate' to **A** and is equal to the transposed matrix of the cofactors. The reciprocal matrix can, accordingly, be expressed in terms of the determinant of the matrix and the cofactor of each matrix element.

The solution of (17.1) can also be expressed in terms of the cofactors.

$$\begin{aligned} x_j = \sum_k a_{jk}^{-1} y_k &= (\det \mathbf{A})^{-1} \Big(\sum_k \tilde{\alpha}_{jk} y_k \Big) \\ &= (\det \mathbf{A})^{-1} \sum_k (y_k \alpha_{kj}) \end{aligned} \tag{17.4}$$

According to exercise 4, Chapter 4 the last sum is equal to the determinant of a matrix derived from **A** by substituting **y** for $\mathbf{a}_{\cdot j}$ or, equally, from the transpose of this matrix. The solution of (17.1) is then written as

$$x_j = \begin{vmatrix} a_{11} & \dots & a_{1(j-1)} & y_1 & a_{1(j+1)} & \dots & a_{1n} \\ \cdot & & & \cdot & & & \cdot \\ \cdot & & & \cdot & & & \cdot \\ \cdot & & & \cdot & & & \cdot \\ a_{n1} & \dots & a_{n(j-1)} & y_n & a_{n(j+1)} & \dots & a_{nn} \end{vmatrix} (\det \mathbf{A})^{-1} \tag{17.5}$$

This formula is known as Cramer's formula for solving linear equations. It is obviously restricted to matrices with non-vanishing determinants. A simple application is shown in (10.8).

Solutions of linear equations can, accordingly, be frequently expressed in terms of determinants. The use of this representation is limited since the evaluation of determinants is hardly less cumbersome than the conventional solution by elimination.

18. Determinant and trace of matrix products

The determinant of a matrix product (**AB**) is, by (13.A) and (16.1) a polynomial in the matrix elements of **A** and **B**. Whatever the coefficients of this polynomial may be they must not depend upon the numerical values of det **A** or of det **B**. In investigating the form of the determinant we are free to make any arbitrary assumption regarding det **A** or det **B**.

Thus let det **B** be zero. By (15.C) the equation $\mathbf{Bx} = 0$ has non-vanishing solutions. The equation $\mathbf{ABx} = 0$ accordingly also has non-vanishing solutions and, by (15.C), det $(\mathbf{AB}) = 0$, for every matrix **A**. This is possible only if det **B** is a factor of det (**AB**).

Let now det $\mathbf{B} \neq 0$ and det $\mathbf{A} = 0$. Then the equation $\mathbf{Bx} = \mathbf{y}$ is uniquely soluble for every **y**. This vector may be chosen in such a way that it solves the equation $\mathbf{Ay} = 0$ without being a null vector. It follows then that

$$\mathbf{ABx} = \mathbf{Ay} = 0$$

for $\mathbf{x} \neq 0$ and therefore det $(\mathbf{AB}) = 0$. Therefore det **A** must be a factor of det (**AB**). Thus

$$\det(\mathbf{AB}) = \lambda(\det \mathbf{A})(\det \mathbf{B})$$

where λ is a scalar multiplier and independent of the two determinants. By setting $\mathbf{A} = \mathbf{B} = \mathbf{AB} = \mathbf{I}$ this factor is identified as being equal to unity.

THEOREM (18.A) The determinant of a matrix product is equal to the product of the determinants of the individual matrices.

It follows that

$$\det(\mathbf{AB}) = \det(\mathbf{BA})$$

even if

$$\mathbf{AB} \neq \mathbf{BA}$$

The trace of a matrix product (**AB**) is the sum of the diagonal elements, i.e.

$$\operatorname{tr}(\mathbf{AB}) = \sum_{j,k} a_{jk} b_{kj} \tag{18.1}$$

Similarly,

$$\operatorname{tr}(\mathbf{BA}) = \sum_{j,k} b_{jk} a_{kj} \tag{18.2}$$

(18.1) and (18.2) differ from each other only by the symbols used for the dummy subscripts and must, therefore, be equal to each other.

$$\text{tr}(\mathbf{AB}) = \text{tr}(\mathbf{BA}) \tag{18.3}$$

even if

$$\mathbf{AB} \neq \mathbf{BA}$$

Up to this stage the concepts of vectors and matrices were used in the first instance as auxiliary devices in the theory of equations. Results obtained will now be used for a further study of the properties of matrices.

EXERCISES

1. Given the matrices

$$\mathbf{A} = \begin{bmatrix} 1 & 0 & 1 \\ 2 & 1 & 2 \\ 0 & 1 & 2 \end{bmatrix} \quad \text{and} \quad \mathbf{B} = \begin{bmatrix} 1 & 1 & 2 \\ 0 & 2 & 0 \\ 1 & 2 & 1 \end{bmatrix}$$

calculate **AB** and **BA**. Show that the traces and the determinants of the products are equal.

2. Given the matrices

$$\mathbf{C} = \begin{bmatrix} 1 & 0 & 2 \\ 1 & 1 & -1 \\ 2 & -1 & 1 \end{bmatrix} \quad \text{and} \quad \mathbf{D} = \begin{bmatrix} 1 & 0 & 0 \\ 0 & 0 & 1 \\ 0 & 1 & 0 \end{bmatrix}$$

derive their squares and cubes. Show that $\det(\mathbf{C}^3) = (\det \mathbf{C})^3$.

3. Prove that the determinants of reciprocal matrices must be reciprocals.

4. Show that

$$e^{a\mathbf{D}} = \begin{bmatrix} \cosh a + \sinh a & 0 & 0 \\ 0 & \cosh a & \sinh a \\ 0 & \sinh a & \cosh a \end{bmatrix}$$

where **D** is defined in exercise 2.

5. Applying matrix multiplication show that

$$\frac{1}{8}\begin{bmatrix} -1 & 1 & 1 & 3 \\ 3 & -1 & 1 & 1 \\ 1 & 3 & -1 & 1 \\ 1 & 1 & 3 & -1 \end{bmatrix}$$

is the reciprocal of

$$\begin{bmatrix} -1 & 2 & 1 & 0 \\ 0 & -1 & 2 & 1 \\ 1 & 0 & -1 & 2 \\ 2 & 1 & 0 & -1 \end{bmatrix}$$

6. Verify the validity of the rule (17.5) by applying it to equations (6.1).

CHAPTER 6

TRANSFORMATIONS

19. Definition

From now on the multiplication of a matrix into a vector will no longer be associated with the solution of equations. In the relation

$$\mathbf{y} = \mathbf{A}\mathbf{x} \tag{19.1}$$

the matrix represents a function by which the independent vector variable $\mathbf{x}$ is converted into the dependent variable $\mathbf{y}$, a 'linear vector function'. We will occasionally write $(\mathbf{A}\mathbf{x})$ with a bracket as a column vector without changing the meaning of $\mathbf{A}$ or $\mathbf{x}$.

The scalar product of a row vector $\tilde{\mathbf{z}}$ and a column vector $\mathbf{A}\mathbf{x}$ is a scalar function of two vectors and called a 'bilinear form'

$$Q(z, x) = \tilde{\mathbf{z}}^*(\mathbf{A}\mathbf{x}) = (\tilde{\mathbf{z}}\mathbf{A})^*\mathbf{x} \tag{19.2}$$

In terms of components

$$Q(z, x) = \sum_j \sum_k \tilde{z}_j^* a_{jk} x_k$$

The simplest bilinear form is the scalar product of two vectors which can be written as $\tilde{\mathbf{z}}(\mathbf{I}\mathbf{x})$.

Expressions of the type (19.1) and (19.2) are used frequently. Their properties depend upon relations between the elements of the matrix $\mathbf{A}$.

The description of any physical object may involve a number of vectors $\mathbf{x}_1$, $\mathbf{x}_2$ .... By means of a matrix $\mathbf{T}$ an alternative set of vectors is defined by

$$\mathbf{x}_j' = \mathbf{T}\mathbf{x}_j \tag{19.3}$$

and may be used for describing the same object. Then all mathematical relations involving the original vectors are converted into relations involving the vectors $\mathbf{x}_j'$. The relation between the two sets of vectors has the form (19.1) but does not establish any relation between different quantities but rather between different specifications of the same vectors; this is called a transformation. If the $\mathbf{x}_j$ and $\mathbf{x}'_j$ are space vectors a transformation is associated with the transition from one to another set of coordinates.

Transformations are of particular importance in studying the properties of functions of vectors. In transforming the vectors in (19.1) or (19.2) it is necessary to transform the matrices simultaneously.

Thus the transformation of equation (19.1) (with $\mathbf{x} = \mathbf{T}\mathbf{x}'$, $\mathbf{y} = \mathbf{T}\mathbf{y}'$)

$$\mathbf{T}\mathbf{y}' = \mathbf{A}\mathbf{T}\mathbf{x}'$$

assuming that det $\mathbf{T} \neq 0$, gives

$$\mathbf{y}' = \mathbf{A}'\mathbf{x}'$$

where
$$\mathbf{A}' = \mathbf{T}^{-1}\mathbf{A}\mathbf{T} \tag{19.4}$$

The transformation (19.3) of a column vector implies that row vectors are transformed by

$$\tilde{\mathbf{z}} = \tilde{\mathbf{z}}'\mathbf{T} \tag{19.5}$$

so that

$$Q(z, x) = (\tilde{\mathbf{z}}'\tilde{\mathbf{T}})^*(\mathbf{A}\mathbf{T}\mathbf{x}') = \tilde{\mathbf{z}}'^*(\mathbf{T}^\dagger\mathbf{A}\mathbf{T}\mathbf{x}') = \tilde{\mathbf{z}}'^*(\mathbf{A}''\mathbf{x}')$$

where
$$\mathbf{A}'' = \mathbf{T}^\dagger\mathbf{A}\mathbf{T} \tag{19.6}$$

Equations (19.4) and (19.6) define 'collineatory' and 'congruent' matrix transformations respectively. Both depend on the use of a transformation matrix $\mathbf{T}$. They can be inverted by the use of $\mathbf{T}^{-1}$ and $\mathbf{T}^\dagger$ respectively.

Examples

1. If the transformation matrix is a diagonal matrix the result of a collineatory transformation $\mathbf{A}' = \mathbf{T}^{-1}\mathbf{A}\mathbf{T}$ has a particularly simple form:

$$a'_{jk} = a_{jk}(t_{kk}/t_{jj})$$

2. Permutations or linear combinations of matrix elements are arrived at by suitable congruent transformations $\mathbf{A}' = \mathbf{T}^\dagger\mathbf{A}\mathbf{T}$.

If $t_{kk} = t_{hh} = 0, \quad t_{hk} = t_{kh} = 1,$
$t_{jl} = \delta_{jl} \quad (j \neq h, j \neq k, l \neq h, l \neq k)$

then

$$a'_{hk} = a_{kh}; \quad a'_{kh} = a_{hk}; \quad a'_{kk} = a_{hh}; \quad a'_{hh} = a_{kk} \quad a'_{jl} = a_{jl}$$

If $t_{hh} = t_{kk} = t_{hk} = t_{hk} = 1, \quad t_{jl} = \delta_{jl}$ as before

then

$$a'_{hh} = a'_{kk} = a'_{hk} = a'_{kh} = a_{hh} + a_{kk} + a_{hk} + a_{kh} \quad a'_{jl} = a_{jl}$$

20. Special types of matrix

The two vectors in the bilinear form (19.2) do not enter in a symmetric way.

$$Q(x, z) = \tilde{\mathbf{x}}^*(\mathbf{Az}) = (\mathbf{A}^\dagger\mathbf{x})^*\mathbf{z} \tag{20.1}$$

This is verified by expressing the right-hand side of (20.1) in terms of components

$$\sum_k \sum_j (a_{kj}^\dagger x_j)^* z_k = \sum_j \sum_k x_j^* a_{jk} z_k$$

which is equal to the left-hand side. Specific properties are to be expected of those bilinear forms in which the matrix may operate *ad libitum* on either vector. This is possible if

$$\mathbf{A}^\dagger = \mathbf{A} \tag{20.2}$$

Matrices complying with the condition (20.2) are called Hermitean. In terms of components (20.2) demands that the diagonal elements of $\mathbf{A}$ be real and that corresponding non-diagonal elements are the conjugate complex of each other: $a_{kj}^* = a_{jk}$. If $\mathbf{A}$ is Hermitean and $\mathbf{z} = \mathbf{x}$ then

$$Q(x, x) = \tilde{\mathbf{x}}^*(\mathbf{Ax})$$

and is accordingly written without brackets as

$$Q(x, x) = \tilde{\mathbf{x}}^*\mathbf{Ax} \tag{20.3}$$

$Q(x, x)$ is called a Hermitean form and is real, even if $\mathbf{x}$ has complex components. If $\mathbf{A}$ in (19.1) is a Hermitean matrix then

$$\mathbf{y} = (\partial/\partial\mathbf{x}^*)(\tilde{\mathbf{y}}^*\mathbf{Ax})$$

meaning that every component of $\mathbf{y}$ is derived from a linear form by differentiating with respect to the corresponding components of $\mathbf{x}^*$. If the elements of a Hermitean matrix are real it is called real-symmetric and the corresponding $Q(x, x)$ with real vectors $\mathbf{x}$ is called a quadratic form.

Apart from the Hermitean matrix another type of matrix is important in connection with matrix transformations. The transformations (19.4) and (19.6) become equal to each other if the transformation matrix satisfies the condition:

$$\mathbf{U}^\dagger = \mathbf{U}^{-1} \tag{20.4}$$

Matrices of this type are called unitary and can be defined by

$$\mathbf{U}^\dagger\mathbf{U} = \mathbf{I} \tag{20.5}$$

or

$$\sum_k u_{jk}^\dagger u_{km} = \sum_k u_{kj}^* u_{km} = \delta_{jm} \tag{20.6}$$

The column vectors of unitary matrices are accordingly normalized vectors and are mutually orthogonal:

$$\sum_k |u_{kj}|^2 = 1 \qquad \sum_k u^*_{kj}u_{km} = 0 \quad (j \neq m)$$

If the elements of a unitary matrix are real the matrix is called real-orthogonal.

THEOREM (20.A) If in a unitary matrix all the non-diagonal elements of any column vanish the non-diagonal elements of the corresponding row must also vanish.

Let $u_{kj} = 0$ for a fixed j and $k \neq j$. Then by (20.6)

$$\sum_k u^*_{kj}u_{kj} = |u_{jj}|^2 = 1$$

This implies that $u_{jj} \neq 0$, but, by (20.6) for $l \neq j$

$$\sum_k u^*_{kj}u_{kl} = u^*_{jj}u_{jl} = 0$$

This implies that $u_{jl} = 0$.

Subsequently we shall be concerned almost exclusively with Hermitean and unitary matrices; other types are of less importance. One should, however, mention complex-orthogonal matrices. They are not unitary; a matrix $\mathbf{C}$ is said to be complex-orthogonal if

$$\tilde{\mathbf{C}} = \mathbf{C}^{-1} \tag{20.7}$$

or

$$\sum_k c_{kj}c_{km} = \delta_{jm} \tag{20.8}$$

A relation between Hermitean and unitary matrices is established by the following theorem.

THEOREM (20.B) If $\mathbf{A}$ is a Hermitean matrix then $\mathbf{V} = e^{i\mathbf{A}}$ is unitary.

Proof

$$\mathbf{V} = \mathbf{I} + \sum_{n=1}^{\infty} (i\mathbf{A})^n/n! = e^{i\mathbf{A}}$$

and

$$\mathbf{V}^\dagger = \mathbf{I} + \sum_{n=1}^{\infty} (-i\mathbf{A})^n/n! = e^{-i\mathbf{A}}$$

As all powers of $\mathbf{A}$ commute with each other and with $\mathbf{I}$ the series defining $\mathbf{V}$ and $\mathbf{V}^\dagger$ can be evaluated as though the matrices were ordinary numbers. Hence

$$\mathbf{V}\mathbf{V}^\dagger = e^{i\mathbf{A}}\, e^{-i\mathbf{A}} = \mathbf{I}$$

so that $\mathbf{V}$ is proved to be unitary.

The determinant of any matrix $\mathbf{G}$ can be written in terms of a modulus m and a phase ϕ:

$$\det \mathbf{G} = m\, e^{i\phi}$$

The determinants of the transposed, adjoint and reciprocal matrices are then

$$\det \widetilde{\mathbf{G}} = m\, e^{i\phi} \qquad \det \mathbf{G}^{\dagger} = m\, e^{-i\phi}$$

$$\det \mathbf{G}^{-1} = (1/m)\, e^{-i\phi}$$

For an Hermitean matrix

$$m\, e^{i\phi} = m\, e^{-i\phi}$$

so that $$\phi = 0, \pi$$

For any unitary matrix

$$m\, e^{-i\phi} = (1/m)\, e^{-i\phi}$$

so that $$|\, m\,|^2 = m = 1$$

For any real- or complex-orthogonal matrix

$$m\, e^{i\phi} = (1/m)\, e^{-i\phi}$$

so that $$\phi = 0, \pi \quad \text{and} \quad m^2 = m = 1$$

THEOREM (20.C) It follows that the determinant of any Hermitean matrix is real, the determinant of a unitary matrix is any complex number of modulus unity, and the determinant of any real- or complex-orthogonal matrix is equal to ± 1.

THEOREM (20.D) The product of two Hermitean matrices is Hermitean if the factors commute.

Let $\mathbf{A}^{\dagger} = \mathbf{A}$, $\mathbf{B}^{\dagger} = \mathbf{B}$. By (16.7), $(\mathbf{AB})^{\dagger} = \mathbf{B}^{\dagger}\mathbf{A}^{\dagger} = \mathbf{BA}$. Hence $(\mathbf{AB})^{\dagger} = \mathbf{AB}$ if $\mathbf{AB} = \mathbf{BA}$.

The product of non-commuting Hermitean matrices is not Hermitean.

THEOREM (20.E) If $\mathbf{A}$ and $\mathbf{B}$ are Hermitean matrices the product $\mathbf{C} = \mathbf{BAB}$ is also Hermitean.

Proof

$$\mathbf{C}^{\dagger} = \mathbf{B}^{\dagger}\mathbf{A}^{\dagger}\mathbf{B}^{\dagger} = \mathbf{BAB} = \mathbf{C}$$

THEOREM (20.F) The product of unitary matrices is unitary.

Let $\mathbf{U}$ and $\mathbf{V}$ be unitary so that $\mathbf{U}^{\dagger} = \mathbf{U}^{-1}$, $\mathbf{V}^{\dagger} = \mathbf{V}^{-1}$. By (16.7) $(\mathbf{UV})^{\dagger} = \mathbf{V}^{\dagger}\mathbf{U}^{\dagger} = \mathbf{V}^{-1}\mathbf{U}^{-1}$. Then $(\mathbf{UV})(\mathbf{UV})^{\dagger} = \mathbf{UVV}^{-1}\mathbf{U}^{-1} = \mathbf{I}$, proving the unitary property of the product.

THEOREM (20.G) The product of complex-orthogonal matrices is complex-orthogonal.

Let $\mathbf{C}$, $\mathbf{D}$ be complex-orthogonal so that $\widetilde{\mathbf{C}} = \mathbf{C}^{-1}$, $\widetilde{\mathbf{D}} = \mathbf{D}^{-1}$. By (16.6) $(\widetilde{\mathbf{CD}}) = \widetilde{\mathbf{D}}\widetilde{\mathbf{C}} = \mathbf{D}^{-1}\mathbf{C}^{-1}$. Then $(\mathbf{CD})(\widetilde{\mathbf{CD}}) = \mathbf{CDD}^{-1}\mathbf{C}^{-1} = \mathbf{I}$, proving the complex-orthogonal property of the product.

Important properties of matrices which are connected with transformations will be considered in the next section.

If $\mathbf{U}$ is a real-orthogonal matrix in three dimensions then

$$\det \mathbf{U} = \pm 1$$

and

$$\begin{aligned} u_{11}^2 + u_{12}^2 + u_{13}^2 &= 1 \quad & u_{11}u_{12} + u_{21}u_{22} + u_{31}u_{32} &= 0 \\ u_{21}^2 + u_{22}^2 + u_{23}^2 &= 1 \quad & u_{12}u_{13} + u_{22}u_{23} + u_{32}u_{33} &= 0 \\ u_{31}^2 + u_{32}^2 + u_{33}^2 &= 1 \quad & u_{13}u_{11} + u_{23}u_{21} + u_{33}u_{31} &= 0 \end{aligned}$$

Assuming that the determinant is positive and applying the expansions (13.1 and 13.2) nine further equations are obtained. If the co-factors are denoted by ω_{jk} we have

$$\sum_k u_{jk}\omega_{lk} = \delta_{jl} \quad \begin{matrix} (j = 1, 2, 3) \\ (l = 1, 2, 3) \end{matrix}$$

For example,

$$u_{11}\omega_{11} + u_{12}\omega_{12} + u_{13}\omega_{13} = 1 \quad \text{and} \quad u_{11}\omega_{21} + u_{12}\omega_{22} + u_{13}\omega_{23} = 0$$

As the determinant of the coefficients will not vanish these equations can be solved with the result that $\omega_{jk} = u_{jk}$. If

$$\det \mathbf{U} = -1 \tag{20.9}$$

the solution is

$$\omega_{jk} = -u_{jk} \tag{20.10}$$

The spin matrices $\mathbf{X}, \mathbf{Y}, \mathbf{Z}$ as obtained in (10.1) are Hermitean and obey the following multiplication rules which are readily verified:

$$\begin{aligned} \mathbf{XY} &= -\mathbf{YX} = -\mathrm{i}\mathbf{Z} \\ \mathbf{YZ} &= -\mathbf{ZY} = -\mathrm{i}\mathbf{X} \\ \mathbf{ZX} &= -\mathbf{XZ} = -\mathrm{i}\mathbf{Y} \end{aligned} \tag{20.11}$$

These matrices are 'anticommutative'. One also has

$$\mathbf{X}^2 = \mathbf{Y}^2 = \mathbf{Z}^2 = \mathbf{I} \tag{20.12}$$

If the exponential functions are defined by their sines,

$$e^{a\mathbf{X}} = (\cosh a)\mathbf{I} + (\sinh a)\mathbf{X}; \tag{20.13}$$

similar formulae apply to the exponential functions of $\mathbf{Y}$ and $\mathbf{Z}$. (20.4) and (20.5) are invariant with respect to collineatory transformations.

Anticommutative matrices of higher dimensions can be derived from the spin matrices by direct multiplication. For instance $\mathbf{I} \times \mathbf{X}$, $\mathbf{I} \times \mathbf{Y}$ are 4-dimensional anticommutative matrices.

21. Invariance under transformations

Matrix elements and vector components are changed under transformations but there are functions of these quantities and relations between these quantities which do not change and are said to be invariant under the transformation.

THEOREM (21.A) If $\mathbf{A}'$, $\mathbf{B}'$, $\mathbf{C}'$ are the collinear or congruous transforms of $\mathbf{A}$, $\mathbf{B}$ and $\mathbf{C}$, λ is a scalar and if

$$\mathbf{A} + \lambda\mathbf{B} = \mathbf{C} \tag{21.1}$$

then

$$\mathbf{A}' + \lambda\mathbf{B}' = \mathbf{C}'$$

This is proved by performing the transformation of (21.1) term by term.

THEOREM (21.B) If $\mathbf{A}'$, $\mathbf{B}'$ and $\mathbf{D}'$ are collinear transforms of $\mathbf{A}$, $\mathbf{B}$ and $\mathbf{D}$ and if

$$\mathbf{AB} = \mathbf{D} \tag{21.2}$$

it follows that

$$\mathbf{A}'\mathbf{B}' = \mathbf{D}' \tag{21.3}$$

This is proved by transforming equation (21.2):

$$(\mathbf{AB})' = \mathbf{T}^{-1}\mathbf{ABT} = \mathbf{T}^{-1}\mathbf{ATT}^{-1}\mathbf{BT} = \mathbf{T}^{-1}\mathbf{DT} = \mathbf{A}'\mathbf{B}'$$

As $\mathbf{TT}^{-1} = \mathbf{I}$ the validity of (21.3) follows.

THEOREM (21.C) The determinant and the trace of any matrix is invariant under a collineatory transformation.

By (18.A) and (18.3) the determinant and the trace of matrix products remain unchanged if the order of the factors is commuted. Hence, if $\mathbf{B}$ and $\mathbf{T}$ are arbitrary matrices,

$$\det \mathbf{T} \neq 0, \quad \det \mathbf{B}' = \det [\mathbf{T}^{-1}(\mathbf{BT})] = \det [(\mathbf{BT})\mathbf{T}^{-1}]$$
$$= \det (\mathbf{BTT}^{-1}) = \det \mathbf{B}$$

Also

$$\operatorname{tr} \mathbf{B}' = \operatorname{tr} [\mathbf{T}^{-1}(\mathbf{BT})] = \operatorname{tr} [(\mathbf{BT})\mathbf{T}^{-1}] = \operatorname{tr} (\mathbf{BTT}^{-1}) = \operatorname{tr} \mathbf{B}$$

THEOREM (21.D) The property of a matrix being Hermitean is preserved under any congruent transformation.

Let $\mathbf{A}$ be Hermitean, so that $\mathbf{A}^\dagger = \mathbf{A}$. Its congruous transform is $\mathbf{A}' = \mathbf{T}^\dagger\mathbf{AT}$. By (16.7) and the associative law of multiplication

$$\mathbf{A}'^\dagger = \mathbf{T}^\dagger\mathbf{A}^\dagger\mathbf{T} = \mathbf{T}^\dagger\mathbf{AT} = \mathbf{A}'$$

Hence $\mathbf{A}'$ is Hermitean.

THEOREM (21.E) The property of a matrix being Hermitean or unitary is preserved under unitary transformations.

For Hermitean matrices this follows from (21.D) since unitary transformations are special instances of congruent transformations.

The unitary transform of a unitary matrix is, by (19.6) or (19.4), a product of three unitary matrices. This is unitary in consequence of theorem (20.F).

THEOREM (21.F) The property of a matrix being complex-orthogonal is preserved under collineatory transformations with a complex-orthogonal matrix.

By definition the reciprocal of a complex-orthogonal matrix is complex-orthogonal. By (19.4) the above transform is a product of three complex-orthogonal matrices which is complex-orthogonal by theorem (20.G).

THEOREM (21.G) The scalar product of two vectors is invariant under any unitary transformation of the vectors.

Let $\tilde{\mathbf{a}}$ and $\mathbf{b}$ be an arbitrary row and column vector and $(\mathbf{ab})$ their scalar product. The transformation is performed by $\mathbf{b} = \mathbf{U}\mathbf{b}'$, $\tilde{\mathbf{a}} = \tilde{\mathbf{a}}'\tilde{\mathbf{U}}$, where $\mathbf{U}$ is unitary. Then

$$(\tilde{\mathbf{a}}\mathbf{b}) = ((\tilde{\mathbf{a}}'\tilde{\mathbf{U}})(\mathbf{U}\mathbf{b}')) = (\tilde{\mathbf{a}}'(\mathbf{U}^{\dagger}\mathbf{U}\mathbf{b}')) = (\tilde{\mathbf{a}}'\mathbf{b}')$$

THEOREM (21.H) Let $\tilde{\mathbf{a}}$ and $\mathbf{b}$ be arbitrary row and column vectors and $\mathbf{C}$ a complex-orthogonal matrix. Then the scalar product $(\mathbf{ab})$ is invariant under a transformation of the vectors by the matrix $\mathbf{C}$.

The transformation is performed by $\tilde{\mathbf{a}}^{*} = \tilde{\mathbf{a}}'^{*}\mathbf{C}^{\dagger}$

$$\mathbf{b} = \mathbf{C}\mathbf{b}'$$

$$(\tilde{\mathbf{a}}^{*}\mathbf{b}) = ((\tilde{\mathbf{a}}^{*\prime}\mathbf{C}^{\dagger})(\mathbf{C}\mathbf{b}')) = (\tilde{\mathbf{a}}^{*\prime}(\tilde{\mathbf{C}}\mathbf{C}\mathbf{b}')) = (\tilde{\mathbf{a}}^{*\prime}(\mathbf{C}^{-1}\mathbf{C}\mathbf{b}')) = (\tilde{\mathbf{a}}^{*\prime}\mathbf{b})$$

Real-orthogonal matrices are special instances of unitary and of complex-orthogonal matrices. A real-orthogonal transformation of space vectors corresponds to a rotation of the axes of a Cartesian frame of reference about the origin in such a way that the axes remain orthogonal. By (21.D) and (21.E) the scalar products of vectors are invariant under this transformation. This is a generalization of familiar theory: the length of space vectors and the angles between different space vectors are not affected by rotation of the coordinate axes.

Usually physical significance is assigned to the length and scalar products of vectors but not to the values of their components. The invariance of scalar products of abstract vectors under unitary transformations suggests that important properties of abstract vectors are unitary invariants. One would expect that matrices have important properties in common with their unitary transforms. This is indeed so and will be shown in detail in the following chapter.

If $\mathbf{A}$ and $\mathbf{B}$ are matrices and $\mathbf{AB} = \mathbf{BA}$ the matrices commute. This property is preserved under collineatory transformations on account of (21.B). Again if $\mathbf{C}$ and $\mathbf{D}$ are matrices such that $\mathbf{CD} = -\mathbf{DC}$, they anticommute and this property is also invariant.

EXERCISES

1. Repeat the deductions leading to the theorems (21.D), (21.E), (21.F), (21.G) and (21.H), in terms of matrix elements and vector components.

2. Obtain the unitary transform of

$$\mathbf{A} = \begin{bmatrix} 1 & 0 & 1 \\ 2 & 1 & 2 \\ 0 & 1 & 2 \end{bmatrix}$$

using the transformation matrix

$$\mathbf{U} = \begin{bmatrix} i/\sqrt{2} & \frac{1}{2} & \frac{1}{2} \\ i/\sqrt{2} & -\frac{1}{2} & -\frac{1}{2} \\ 0 & 1/\sqrt{2} & -1/\sqrt{2} \end{bmatrix}$$

Show that the trace of the transformed matrix is equal to the trace of $\mathbf{A}$.

3. Prove that the row vectors of any unitary matrix are normalized and mutually orthogonal.

4. Show that any unitary matrix remains unitary if it is multiplied by a 'phase factor', i.e. a complex number of modulus unity.

5. Identify the Hermitean, unitary or complex-orthogonal property of the following matrices:

$$\begin{bmatrix} 1 & 1 & -i \\ i & \frac{1}{2}i & \frac{3}{2} \\ -1 & \frac{1}{2} & \frac{1}{2}i \end{bmatrix} \qquad \begin{bmatrix} \frac{1}{2} & \frac{1}{2}(1-i) & -\frac{1}{2} \\ \frac{1}{2}(1+i) & 1 & -\frac{1}{3}i \\ -\frac{1}{2} & \frac{1}{3}i & 0 \end{bmatrix}$$

$$\begin{bmatrix} 1/\sqrt{3} & i/\sqrt{6} & i/\sqrt{2} \\ i/\sqrt{3} & 2/\sqrt{6} & 0 \\ 1/\sqrt{3} & i/\sqrt{6} & -i/\sqrt{2} \end{bmatrix}$$

CHAPTER 7

DIAGONALIZATION OF MATRICES

22. The characteristic equation

The subject of this chapter is at first presented in an entirely formal way; its significance is considered in Section 25.

A matrix and a vector may be adapted to each other in such a way that the matrix–vector multiplication has the same effect as multiplying the vector by some scalar, so that

$$\mathbf{A}\mathbf{x} = \alpha\mathbf{x} \tag{22.1}$$

Attempts at identifying the vectors by which equation (22.1) is solved lead to important relations in matrix algebra.

In attempting to solve equation (22.1) it is seen that this is a homogeneous system and has as one solution $\mathbf{x} = 0$. This however does not convey any information on the matrix $\mathbf{A}$. Non-vanishing solutions exist only for selected values of α which are determined by the 'characteristic equation of the matrix $\mathbf{A}$', given in equation

$$\det(\mathbf{A} - \alpha\mathbf{I}) = 0 \tag{22.2}$$

The solutions of this equation are called the *eigenvalues* of A. Equation (22.2) is an algebraic equation of the nth degree in α and has, accordingly, n solutions. They may be complex, even if the matrix elements are real; some of them may be 'degenerate', i.e. multiple roots of (22.2).

Usually the characteristic equation cannot be solved in terms of a closed expression involving the matrix elements. For the computation of the eigenvalues numerical methods have to be employed; approximate solutions can frequently be obtained in algebraic form. This will be considered in Section 27.

Let $\mathbf{T}$ be a matrix which has a reciprocal, so that $\mathbf{A}' = \mathbf{T}^{-1}\mathbf{A}\mathbf{T}$ is a collinear transform of $\mathbf{A}$. Its characteristic equation is

$$\det(\mathbf{T}^{-1}\mathbf{A}\mathbf{T} - \alpha\mathbf{I}) = 0 \tag{22.3}$$

By (18.A) and the definition of reciprocal matrices equation (22.3) can be rearranged:

$$\begin{aligned}\det(\mathbf{T}^{-1}\mathbf{A}\mathbf{T} - \alpha\mathbf{T}^{-1}\mathbf{I}\mathbf{T}) &= (\det \mathbf{T}^{-1})[\det(\mathbf{A} - \alpha\mathbf{I})](\det \mathbf{T})\\ &= \det(\mathbf{A} - \alpha\mathbf{I}) = 0\end{aligned}$$

It is seen that the characteristic equation is invariant with respect to collineatory transformations of the matrix. An important conclusion follows.

THEOREM (22.A) The eigenvalues of any matrix are collineatory invariants.

If an eigenvalue $\alpha_1 \ldots \alpha_n$ is substituted into equation (22.1) it has non-vanishing solutions. The solutions are vectors, denoted by $\mathbf{x}_{\cdot 1} \ldots \mathbf{x}_{\cdot n}$ and are called *eigenvectors* of the matrix $\mathbf{A}$.

In accordance with the arguments in Section 7 the eigenvectors are not uniquely determined; they involve at least an undetermined factor. This factor can, but need not, be fixed by normalization so that $|\mathbf{x}_{\cdot j}|^2 = 1$. Equally, different eigenvectors of a matrix can, but need not, be linearly independent.

It will now be shown that any linear dependence of eigenvectors is possible only if the corresponding eigenvalues are equal to each other.

This is readily demonstrated for two eigenvectors $\mathbf{x}_{\cdot s}$ and $\mathbf{x}_{\cdot s+1}$. If they are linearly dependent so that

$$c_s\mathbf{x}_{\cdot s} + c_{s+1}\mathbf{x}_{\cdot s+1} = 0 \quad (c_s, c_{s+1} \neq 0) \tag{22.4}$$

then, by (22.1) and (22.4),

$$\begin{aligned}\mathbf{A}c_s\mathbf{x}_{\cdot s} &= \alpha_s c_s \mathbf{x}_{\cdot s}\\ \mathbf{A}c_{s+1}\mathbf{x}_{\cdot s+1} &= \alpha_{s+1}c_{s+1}\mathbf{x}_{\cdot s+1} = -\alpha_{s+1}c_s\mathbf{x}_{\cdot s}\end{aligned}$$

and, by adding these equations,

$$(\alpha_s - \alpha_{s+1})c_s\mathbf{x}_s = 0$$

This is possible only if $\alpha_s = \alpha_{s+1}$.

Assuming that the equality of the eigenvalues has been established for r linearly dependent eigenvectors, the equality is now demonstrated for $r + 1$ vectors. Thus let $\mathbf{x}_{\cdot s} \ldots \mathbf{x}_{\cdot s+r}$ be eigenvectors, let $\alpha_s = \alpha_{s+1} = \ldots = \alpha_{s+r+1}$ and

$$\sum_{j=s}^{s+r} c_j\mathbf{x}_{\cdot j} = 0 \quad (c_j \neq 0) \tag{22.5}$$

Then, by (22.1) and (22.4),

$$\begin{aligned}\mathbf{A}c_{s+r}\mathbf{x}_{\cdot s+r} &= \alpha_{s+r}c_{s+r}\mathbf{x}_{s+r}\\ \mathbf{A}\sum_{j=s}^{s+r-1} c_j\mathbf{x}_{\cdot j} &= \alpha_s \sum_{j=s}^{s+r+1} c_j\mathbf{x}_{\cdot j} = -\alpha_s c_{s+r}\mathbf{x}_{\cdot s+r}\end{aligned}$$

and, by adding these equations,

$$(\alpha_{s+r} - \alpha_s)c_{s+r}\mathbf{x}_{\cdot s+r} = 0$$

This is possible only if $\alpha_{s+r} = \alpha_s$.

It follows then that the eigenvalues corresponding to any number of linearly dependent eigenvectors must be equal.

THEOREM (22.B) All eigenvectors of a matrix are linearly independent if they all differ from each other. However, if a set of eigenvectors corresponds to one and the same eigenvalue these vectors may or may not be linearly independent.

23. Collineatory and unitary transformations

Equation (22.1) which determines the eigenvalues and eigenvectors of a matrix can be regarded as a component of a matrix equation

$$\mathbf{AX} = \mathbf{XA}' \tag{23.1}$$

where $\mathbf{X}$ is an unknown matrix and $\mathbf{A}'$ an unknown diagonal matrix. The diagonal elements of $\mathbf{A}'$ are the eigenvalues of $\mathbf{A}$, the columns of $\mathbf{X}$ are its eigenvectors. Provided that $\mathbf{X}$ has a reciprocal (23.1) can be written as a collineatory transformation

$$\mathbf{X}^{-1}\mathbf{AX} = \mathbf{A}' \tag{23.2}$$

where the transform $\mathbf{A}'$ is a diagonal matrix.

By (21.C) the trace and determinant of matrices are collineatory invariants. By (23.2) they are respectively the sum and product of the eigenvalues of $\mathbf{A}$. Therefore these two functions of the eigenvalues can be derived from the matrix $\mathbf{A}$ in its original form without performing the transformation, provided the existence of a transformation matrix is established.

By (15.B) and (17.A) the matrix $\mathbf{X}$ has a reciprocal if the eigenvectors are linearly independent. By (22.B) this condition is complied with if the characteristic equation has no multiple solution. This is sufficient for the existence of a collineatory transformation to the diagonal form.

At this stage a simple example is instructive. Let $\mathbf{A}$ be a 2×2 matrix

$$\mathbf{A} = \begin{bmatrix} a_{11} & a_{12} \\ a_{21} & a_{22} \end{bmatrix} \tag{23.3}$$

Its characteristic equation has the form

$$\alpha^2 - \alpha(a_{11} + a_{22}) + (a_{11}a_{22} - a_{12}a_{21}) = 0$$

The coefficients of this equation are readily identified as the negative trace and the determinant of $\mathbf{A}$. The eigenvalues are

$$\alpha = \tfrac{1}{2}\{+a_{11} + a_{22} \pm [(a_{11} - a_{22})^2 + 4a_{12}a_{21}]^{1/2}\} \tag{23.4}$$

In terms of normalized eigenvectors the transformation matrix can be written as

$$\mathbf{X} = \begin{bmatrix} 2a_{12}/N_1 & 2a_{12}/N_2 \\ N_1^{-1}\{a_{22} - a_{11} & N_2^{-1}\{a_{22} - a_{11} \\ \quad - [(a_{22} - a_{11})^2 & \quad + [(a_{22} - a_{11})^2 \\ \quad + 4a_{12}a_{21}]^{1/2}\} & \quad + 4a_{12}a_{21}]^{1/2}\} \end{bmatrix} \tag{23.5}$$

where

$$\left.\begin{matrix} N_1^2 \\ N_2^2 \end{matrix}\right\} = 4\,|\,a_{12}\,|^2 + |\,(a_{22} - a_{11}) \mp [(a_{22} - a_{11})^2 + 4a_{12}a_{21}]^{1/2}\,|^2$$

The two eigenvectors are linearly independent unless

$$(a_{22} - a_{11})^2 + 4a_{12}a_{21} = 0.$$

In this case the matrix $\mathbf{X}$ has no reciprocal and $\mathbf{A}$ cannot be diagonalized by any collineatory transformation.

In physics matrices of importance are usually Hermitean or unitary. For matrices of this kind the existence of a transformation matrix can be established even if the characteristic equation has multiple solutions. Moreover the transformation matrix is unitary or may be chosen as unitary. A direct proof of this would require the demonstration of linear independence and orthogonality of the eigenvectors. Here an alternative argument is put forward: it will be shown that a unitary transformation matrix can be constructed by a finite set of well-defined algebraic operations.

A Hermitean or a unitary matrix $\mathbf{A}$ is to be transformed to

$$\mathbf{A}' = \mathbf{U}^{-1}\mathbf{A}\mathbf{U} \tag{23.6}$$

where $\mathbf{U}$ is unitary and $\mathbf{A}'$ is diagonal. The transformation matrix is expressed as a product of unitary matrices

$$\mathbf{U} = \mathbf{U}^{(1)}\mathbf{U}^{(2)}\mathbf{U}^{(3)}\mathbf{U}^{(4)} \ldots \mathbf{U}^{(n-1)} \tag{23.7}$$

The matrix $\mathbf{U}^{(j)}$ is formed from two sub-matrices, a $(j-1)$-dimensional unit matrix and an $(n+1-j)$-dimensional unitary sub-matrix to be denoted by $\mathbf{V}^{(j)}$; $\mathbf{V}^{(1)} = \mathbf{U}^{(1)}$. The matrix elements of $\mathbf{U}^{(j)}$ which are outside the two sub-matrices are assumed to be zero.

$$\mathbf{U}^{(j)} = \left[\begin{array}{c|c} \mathbf{I} & 0 \\ \hline 0 & \mathbf{V}^{(j)} \end{array}\right] \tag{23.8}$$

It is readily verified that the matrix (23.8) is unitary for every j.

The following transforms of $\mathbf{A}$ are now defined

$$\begin{aligned} &\mathbf{A}^{(j)} = \mathbf{U}^{(j)-1}\mathbf{A}^{(j-1)}\mathbf{U}^{(j)} \quad (j = 1 \ldots (n-1)) \\ &\mathbf{A}^{(0)} = \mathbf{A}; \quad \mathbf{A}^{n-1} = \mathbf{A}' \end{aligned} \tag{23.9}$$

It is attempted to determine these transforms such that they consist of two sub-matrices, all elements outside these being zero. One sub-matrix is taken to be a diagonal matrix $\mathbf{D}^{(j)}$ of j dimensions, the other has $n - j$ dimensions and is denoted by $\mathbf{B}^{(j)}$.

$$\mathbf{A}^{(j)} = \begin{bmatrix} \mathbf{D}^{(j)} & 0 \\ 0 & \mathbf{B}^{(j)} \end{bmatrix} \tag{23.10}$$

By theorem (21.E) the matrices $\mathbf{A}^{(j)}$ and all their sub-matrices are Hermitean or unitary if $\mathbf{A}$ is Hermitean or unitary respectively. Also by (22.3) the characteristic equation of all the transforms of $\mathbf{A}$ are identical so that the diagonal elements of $\mathbf{D}^{(j)}$ and the eigenvalues of $\mathbf{B}^{(j)}$ are eigenvalues of $\mathbf{A}$.

The transformation (23.9) leaves the sub-matrix $\mathbf{D}^{(j-1)}$ unchanged and transforms the sub-matrix $\mathbf{B}^{(j-1)}$ according to

$$\mathbf{B}^{(j)} = \mathbf{V}^{(j)-1}\mathbf{B}^{(j-1)}\mathbf{V}^{(j)} \tag{23.11}$$

In order to comply with (23.10) the effect of the transformation (23.11) must be a substitution of zero for the non-diagonal elements in the jth rows and columns of $\mathbf{B}^{(j-1)}$. It is, in fact, sufficient to show that this substitution is made in the columns; the corresponding substitution in the rows then follows, for Hermitean matrices on account of their definition, for unitary matrices by theorem (20.A).

In order to prove that an appropriate transformation matrix exists it is sufficient to exhibit an appropriate matrix $\mathbf{U}^{(1)}$; construction of the subsequent transformation matrices does not involve any additional problems.

Let α_1 be an eigenvalue of $\mathbf{A}$; the corresponding normalized eigenvector—which need not be defined uniquely—is then the first column of $\mathbf{U}^{(1)}$. The first column of $\mathbf{A}^{(1)}$ is given by

$$a_{h1}^{(1)} = \sum_k \sum_m u_{hk}^{(1)-1} a_{km} u_{m1}^{(1)} = \sum_k u_{hk}^{(1)-1} u_{k1}^{(1)} \alpha_1 = \alpha_1 \delta_{h1}$$

in accordance with (23.8). In order to complete the proof it is necessary to demonstrate the existence of a unitary matrix $\mathbf{U}^{(1)}$. The precise values of the matrix elements in the 2nd to nth columns are not relevant. These column vectors can accordingly be deduced from any set of $n - 1$ vectors which, together with $\mathbf{u}_{\cdot 1}^{(1)}$ are a set of linearly independent vectors. These $n - 1$ vectors may be, for instance, of the form (2.3). The set of linearly independent vectors is converted to a set of orthogonal normalized vectors by the use of equations (3.5). Thus the matrix $\mathbf{U}^{(1)}$ is shown to exist.

As a conclusion two theorems can be formulated.

THEOREM (23.A) Hermitean and unitary matrices can be diagonalized by a unitary transformation.

THEOREM (23.B) The eigenvalues of Hermitean matrices are real; the eigenvalues of unitary matrices have a modulus equal to unity.

This follows from the definitions and from theorem (21.E). It is not difficult to show that real symmetric matrices can be diagonalized by real-orthogonal transformation matrices.

It follows from the unitary invariance of the trace and determinant of matrices that the trace is the sum of the eigenvalues and the determinant their product. As an example of a Hermitean matrix consider (23.3), assuming that a_{11} and a_{22} are real and $a_{21} = a_{12}^*$. Then $(a_{11} - a_{22})^2 + 4a_{12}a_{21}$ is necessarily positive so that the eigenvalues (23.4) must be real. The scalar product of the eigenvectors is, according to (23.5)

$$(\mathbf{x}_{\cdot 1}\mathbf{x}_{\cdot 2}) = \frac{1}{N_1 N_2}\{4 \mid a_{12} \mid^2 + (a_{22} - a_{11})^2 - [(a_{22} - a_{11})^2 + 4 \mid a_{12} \mid^2]\} = 0$$

so that the matrix $\mathbf{X}$ is proved unitary.

A simple example for a unitary matrix is

$$\mathbf{C} = \begin{bmatrix} c\,e^{i\phi} & (1 - c^2)^{1/2} \\ (1 - c^2)^{1/2} & -c\,e^{-i\phi} \end{bmatrix}$$

where c and ϕ are real and $0 < c < 1$. The eigenvalues are

$$\gamma = \pm(1 - c^2 \sin^2 \phi)^{1/2} + ic \sin \phi$$

Their modulus square is equal to unity. The transformation matrix is

$$\mathbf{X} = \begin{bmatrix} 2(1 - c^2)^{1/2}/N_1 & 2(1 - c^2)^{1/2}/N_2 \\ -2N_1^{-1}[c \cos \phi + (1 - c^2 \sin^2 \phi)] & 2N_2^{-1}[c \cos \phi + (1 - c^2 \sin^2 \phi)] \end{bmatrix}$$

It can be verified that the eigenvectors are orthogonal.

THEOREM (23.C) If $\mathbf{A}$ and $\mathbf{B}$ are Hermitean matrices with non-negative eigenvalues the eigenvalues of $\mathbf{A} + \mathbf{B}$ must also be non-negative.

Let $\mathbf{U}$ be a unitary matrix and $\mathbf{A}' = \mathbf{U}^{-1}\mathbf{A}\mathbf{U}$ be diagonal. Then the diagonal elements of $\mathbf{A}$ are

$$a_{jj} = \sum_k u_{jk} a'_{kk} u_{kj}^{-1} = \sum_k a'_{kk} \mid u_{jk} \mid^2$$

and they are according to premises non-negative. By a similar argument it follows that the diagonal elements of all unitary transforms of $\mathbf{A}$ are non-negative.

The sum $\mathbf{A} + \mathbf{B}$ is Hermitean. The diagonal elements of $\mathbf{A}$ and of

B are accordingly non-negative and if **V** is unitary the diagonal elements of $\mathbf{V}^{-1}\mathbf{A}\mathbf{V} + \mathbf{V}^{-1}\mathbf{B}\mathbf{V} = \mathbf{V}^{-1}(\mathbf{A} + \mathbf{B})\mathbf{V}$ are also non-negative. Hence, if **V** is the matrix diagonalizing $\mathbf{A} + \mathbf{B}$, the resulting diagonal elements are the eigenvalues and must be non-negative.

24. Congruent transformations

Hermitean matrices can be diagonalized by congruent transformations which are not unitary. These transformations are not so important as those considered in the preceding section but are useful in various contexts.

Let **A** be a Hermitean matrix, **T** a transformation matrix and $\mathbf{A}' = \mathbf{T}^{\dagger}\mathbf{A}\mathbf{T}$ be a diagonal matrix. Let **T** be a product of the form (23.7) where **T** and $\mathbf{T}^{(j)}$ are substituted for **U** and $\mathbf{U}^{(j)}$ respectively. The matrices $\mathbf{T}^{(j)}$ have the form (23.8) but $\mathbf{V}^{(j)}$ is not unitary. Transforms of **A** are defined according to (23.9) with $\mathbf{T}^{(j)}$ and $\mathbf{T}^{(j)\dagger}$ substituted for $\mathbf{U}^{(j)}$ and $\mathbf{U}^{(j)-1}$; these transforms are Hermitean. It is attempted to obtain them in the form (23.10), but the diagonal elements of $\mathbf{D}^{(j)}$ are not derived from the characteristic equation and not related in any simple way to the eigenvalues of **A**. The submatrices $\mathbf{B}^{(j)}$ are transformed according to (23.11) with $\mathbf{V}^{(j)\dagger}$ substituted for $\mathbf{V}^{(j)-1}$.

So far the procedure is completely analogous to the corresponding argument in Section 23; however, the matrices are not derived from eigenvectors. Neither the transformation nor the resulting matrix **A**′ are uniquely defined.

The matrices $\mathbf{T}^{(j)}$ and $\mathbf{V}^{(j)}$ can be, but need not be, defined according to

$$t_{11}^{(1)} = 1; \quad t_{1k}^{(1)} = -a_{1k}/a_{11}; \qquad t_{mk}^{(1)} = \delta_{mk}\,(m > 1)$$
$$v_{jj}^{(j)} = 1; \quad v_{jk}^{(j)} = -b_{jk}^{(j-1)}/b_{jj}^{(j-1)}; \quad b_{mk}^{(j)} = \delta_{mk}\,(m > j)$$

These definitions are applicable only if a_{11} and the $b_{jj}^{(j-1)}$ do not vanish. Alternative transformation matrices are defined after performing a preliminary congruent transformation by which matrix elements are permuted or linearly combined (see Section 19, example 2).

The following transformations are of greater importance. Let **A** and **B** be Hermitean matrices and let **B** comply with the condition that all its eigenvalues b_{jj}' are positive. It follows then that the matrix $\mathbf{B}^{1/2}$ is also Hermitean and that both **B** and $\mathbf{B}^{1/2}$ have a Hermitean reciprocal. Thus the two matrices are transformed by a common congruent transformation.

$$\mathbf{A}' = \mathbf{B}^{-1/2}\mathbf{A}\mathbf{B}^{-1/2} \qquad \mathbf{B}' = \mathbf{B}^{-1/2}\mathbf{B}\mathbf{B}^{-1/2} = \mathbf{I}$$

The matrix **A**′ is Hermitean, by theorem (20.D); the matrix **B**′ is diagonal and invariant under all unitary transformations. In the next stage $\mathbf{A}'$ is diagonalized by a unitary transformation:

$$\mathbf{A}'' = \mathbf{W}^{-1}\mathbf{A}'\mathbf{W} = \mathbf{W}^{\dagger}\mathbf{A}'\mathbf{W}$$

whereas $\mathbf{B}'$ remains unchanged under this transformation. Thus both matrices have been diagonalized by a congruent transformation. The transformation matrix is $\mathbf{T} = \mathbf{B}^{-1/2}\mathbf{W}$. It is not necessary and it would be cumbersome to derive $\mathbf{B}^{-1/2}$ or $\mathbf{B}'$ explicitly. Instead it is noted that the collineatory transformation

$$\mathbf{B}^{-1/2}\mathbf{A}'\mathbf{B}^{1/2} = \mathbf{B}^{-1}\mathbf{A}$$

converts $\mathbf{A}'$ to $\mathbf{B}^{-1}\mathbf{A}$. By (22.A) the eigenvalues of $\mathbf{A}'$ are equal to the eigenvalues of $\mathbf{B}^{-1}\mathbf{A}$. One can accordingly start with the equation determining the eigenvectors of $\mathbf{B}^{-1}\mathbf{A}$:

$$\mathbf{B}^{-1}\mathbf{A}\mathbf{x} = \gamma\mathbf{x}$$

or

$$\mathbf{A}\mathbf{x} = \gamma\mathbf{B}\mathbf{x}$$

The eigenvalues of $\mathbf{B}^{-1}\mathbf{A}$ are accordingly determined by the characteristic equation

$$\det(\mathbf{A} - \gamma\mathbf{B}) = 0 \tag{24.1}$$

It is a more involved structure than the characteristic equations of single matrices since every term of the determinant depends on the unknown γ.

In this problem the eigenvectors $\mathbf{x}$ are not connected with the transformation matrix $\mathbf{T}$. In order to find the latter it may be convenient to remember that $(\mathbf{A}')^2 = \mathbf{B}^{-1}\mathbf{A}^2\mathbf{B}$ can be calculated by matrix multiplication, that eigenvectors of $\mathbf{A}'$ are identical with eigenvectors of $(\mathbf{A}')^2$ and that the eigenvalues of $(\mathbf{A}')^2$ are the squares of the quantities γ as obtained from (24.1).

This result is applicable to Hermitean (or real quadratic) forms. If $\mathbf{A}$ is Hermitean $Q(x, x) = \tilde{\mathbf{x}}^*\mathbf{A}\mathbf{x}$, and $\mathbf{x} = \mathbf{T}\mathbf{x}'$, then $Q = \tilde{\mathbf{x}}^{*\prime}\mathbf{A}'\mathbf{x}'$ and, if $\mathbf{A}'$ is a diagonal matrix, then Q is converted to a sum of moduli squares, or squares, respectively.

As this congruent transformation can be performed in different ways it is possible to select particular transformations by subsidiary conditions. In particular one can diagonalize two matrices simultaneously so that two Hermitean or quadratic forms can be simultaneously converted to sums of moduli squares, or squares.

In conclusion it may be of interest to point out a remarkable property of Hermitean forms. Regarding $Q(x, x)$ as a function of the vectors $\tilde{\mathbf{x}}$ and $\mathbf{x}$, let these vectors be varied, subject to the condition that $|\mathbf{x}|^2$ remains fixed. The corresponding values of Q will include maximum and minimum and saddle points. They can be identified by setting the differential of Q equal to zero.

$$\begin{aligned}(\partial/\partial\mathbf{x})(Q - \alpha\,|\,\mathbf{x}\,|^2) &= \tilde{\mathbf{x}}\mathbf{A} - \alpha\tilde{\mathbf{x}} = 0 \\ (\partial/\partial\mathbf{x}^*)(Q - \alpha\,|\,\mathbf{x}\,|^2) &= \mathbf{A}\mathbf{x} - \alpha\mathbf{x} = 0\end{aligned} \tag{24.2}$$

Here α is a Lagrange multiplier, introduced in order to maintain the fixed value of $|\mathbf{x}|^2$. The unfamiliar differentiation with respect to a vector is performed by differentiation with respect to every vector component, the resulting differential coefficients being components of another vector. The result, that is equation (24.2), is the same as equation (22.1) by which eigenvectors are determined. Hence the following theorem is established.

THEOREM (24.A) The maximum and minimum and saddle points of a Hermitean form $\tilde{\mathbf{x}}^* \mathbf{A} \mathbf{x}$ are found by substituting a normalized eigenvector for $\mathbf{x}$; the corresponding values of the Hermitean form are the eigenvalues of $\mathbf{A}$.

25. Discussion

After presenting a number of theorems and rules concerning the transformation of matrices to the diagonal form, it is appropriate to consider their significance and the use that can be made of them.

It may be noticed that, by diagonalization, the specification of matrices is rendered more concise. The number of non-vanishing elements in a diagonal matrix is n, as distinct from the usual n^2. Moreover the eigenvalues of a matrix are common to a whole set of matrices which are mutually related by collineatory transformations. Also, the knowledge of an eigenvector allows one in special instances (cf. (22.1)) to replace a matrix by a single number.

The congruent diagonalization of matrices is frequently helpful because entities in physics and in statistics are often expressible as quadratic or Hermitean forms. They can be transformed to a sum of squares of a single variable only. Frequently the possibility of handling these quadratic forms mathematically depends on the separation of variables by diagonalization.

The multiplication of any pair of diagonal matrices is commutative. By theorem (21.B) this property of the matrices is preserved if both are transformed by one and the same collineatory transformation. As collineatory transformations can be inverted it follows that all pairs of commuting matrices can be diagonalized simultaneously. Thus all powers of a matrix can be diagonalized simultaneously and any matrix polynomial can be diagonalized term by term, implying one and the same transformation matrix.

The same is true for infinite power series as defined in Section 16. For these series the criterion of convergence is most readily formulated if they are diagonalized: every diagonal element consists of a power series in a single variable; the coefficients are the same in all elements and the variable assumes all eigenvalues in succession. The convergence of these series can then be assessed by any accepted criterion. Convergence of the matrix series means that convergence in all diagonal elements is established.

Moreover the method of diagonalization can be used for defining irrational or transcendental functions of matrices without any appeal to expansions in terms of matrix powers. If $f(x)$ is any analytic function and the eigenvalues $(\alpha_1, \ldots \alpha_n)$ of the matrix $\mathbf{A}$ are successively substituted for x, then the diagonal matrix with the elements $f(\alpha_j)$ defines the diagonalized matrix function $f(\mathbf{A})$. It can subsequently be converted to different forms by collineatory transformations.

These mathematical aspects of diagonalization are not sufficient to explain its significance in physics; it will be seen that the eigenvalues of matrices are frequently quantities playing a leading role in physical theories and in their experimental implications, such as the natural frequencies of oscillations. In the following section a special type of matrix is surveyed; even here the concepts of diagonalization will prove indispensable.

26. Projective matrices

The 'projection' of a space vector $\mathbf{r}$ on another vector $\mathbf{s}$ is defined by

$$\mathbf{t} = \mathbf{s}(r/s) \cos \beta \tag{26.1}$$

β being the angle between the two vectors. The magnitude of the projection,

$$t = r \cos \beta \tag{26.2}$$

is the scalar product of r with a unit vector in the direction of s; the vector $\mathbf{t}$ is a multiple of $\mathbf{s}$.

The concept of projection can be applied to abstract vectors as is shown in this section.

Let $\mathbf{A}'$ be a matrix and $\mathbf{A}$ its unitary transform, then

$$a_{hj} = \sum_l \sum_m u_{hl}^{-1} a'_{lm} u_{mj}$$

If $\mathbf{A}'$ is a diagonal matrix, $a'_{lm} = \alpha_l \delta_{lm}$ and therefore

$$a_{hj} = \sum_l u^*_{lh} \alpha_l u_{lj}$$

This can be written as a matrix equation

$$\mathbf{A} = \sum_l \alpha_l \mathbf{P}(l) \tag{26.3}$$

where

$$p_{hj}(l) = u^*_{lh} u_{lj} \tag{26.4}$$

By (26.3) every matrix that can be diagonalized by a unitary transformation admits an expansion progressing in eigenvalues. The expansion coefficients are matrices which can be expressed in terms of eigenvectors. Their properties are readily recognized by squaring equation (26.4),

$$p^2_{hk}(l) = \sum_j p_{hj}(l)p_{jk}(l) = \sum_j u^*_{lh}u_{lj}u^*_{lj}u_{lk}$$
$$= u^*_{lh}u_{lk} = p_{hk}(l)$$

or

$$\mathbf{P}^2(l) = \mathbf{P}(l) \tag{26.5}$$

All positive powers of $\mathbf{P}(l)$ are, accordingly, equal to each other.

The matrices $\mathbf{P}(l)$ are, by (26.4), Hermitean and can accordingly be diagonalized by unitary transformation. Equation (26.5) must be valid before and after diagonalization. It follows that the eigenvalues of $\mathbf{P}(l)$ must be 0 or 1, since only these two numbers are equal to their squares. The trace

$$\text{tr } \mathbf{P}(l) = \sum_h p_{hh}(l) = \sum_h u^*_{lh}u_{lh} = 1$$

Thus there must be a single eigenvalue equal to unity, the others being zero.

Further properties of the matrices $\mathbf{P}(l)$ are derived by considering the product

$$\mathbf{y}(l) = \mathbf{P}(l)\mathbf{x}$$

where $\mathbf{x}$ is an arbitrary vector. This product is evaluated by

$$y_j(l) = \sum_k u^*_{lj}u_{lk}x_k$$

and can be written as

$$\mathbf{y}(l) = \mathbf{u}^*_l(\mathbf{u}^*_l.\mathbf{x}) \tag{26.6}$$

This equation is similar to (26.1). The matrix $\mathbf{P}(l)$ converts the vector $\mathbf{x}$ into a vector proportional to $\mathbf{u}$ which is a unit vector; the magnitude of $\mathbf{y}$ is equal to the scalar product of the two vectors. $\mathbf{y}$ can be regarded as the projection of $\mathbf{x}$ on $\mathbf{u}$. For this reason $\mathbf{P}(l)$ is called a projective matrix. It can be shown that the matrix product $\mathbf{P}(l)\mathbf{P}(m)$ vanishes.

Matrices with eigenvalues 0 and 1 are generally called projective matrices.

27. The practice of diagonalization

Algebraic expressions of the eigenvalues, such as (23.4), can be obtained in exceptional instances only. However, if the matrix elements are given numerically the eigenvalues can be derived numerically to any degree of accuracy. On the other hand there are algebraic methods for approximate diagonalization. Problems of diagonalization can usually be solved by routine methods but may sometimes be a problem for research.

Numerical diagonalization is an extensive subject and could not be dealt with in a volume like the present. However, numerical and approximate algebraical methods have wider implications and some aspects of these methods are accordingly reviewed in the present section.

All numerical procedures for solving algebraic equations of higher degrees are applicable to the characteristic equation. Also, there are methods specially adapted to matrices. As an example consider a technique which is particularly well suited to Hermitean matrices. If the highest eigenvalue is markedly larger than the others the multiplication of a unit vector by a high matrix power will convert it to a multiple of the eigenvector of the highest eigenvalue. It is accordingly convenient to begin with some arbitrary unit vector. This is multiplied by the matrix and the resultant vector is renormalized. After a sufficient number of repetitions, multiplication by the matrix will multiply the vector by a constant factor, which is equal to the highest eigenvalue. The corresponding eigenvector is then readily identified and can be used for constructing the projective matrix as defined by (26.4). By using equation (26.3) it is now possible to construct a matrix which has the same eigenvalues as the original matrix except the highest. If the second highest eigenvalue is larger than the others the method of computation can be repeated.

Numerical or semi-algebraical methods for calculating eigenvalues can be based on theorem (24.A). By putting into a Hermitean form any unit vector the form takes a value higher than the lowest and lower than the highest eigenvalue. By systematically changing the components of the vector in such a way that the value of the form is lowered it is relatively simple to find an approximation to the lowest eigenvalue. The approximation may be good even if the vector itself is not a good approximation to the eigenvector.

It is sometimes possible to reduce the characteristic equation so that it is replaced by a number of equations of lower degree. At first the matrix is transformed in such a way that it divides into sub-matrices that extend equally to each side of the leading diagonal; the sub-matrices have no elements in common and all elements outside the sub-matrices are 0. At a later stage the sub-matrices are diagonalized independently of each other. The first transform is to be identified prior to solving the characteristic equation. This is possible if matrix transformations are linked to transformations of quantities describing physical objects. If an object is, for instance, specified in terms of spatial coordinates and the specification is symmetric with respect to rotations, the appropriate matrix transform can be constructed by means of the theory of group representation or an equivalent theory. These mathematical theories are not considered in this book but their significance will be illustrated by examples (cf. Sections 30 and 33).

If the number of rows and columns is very large and the difference between successive eigenvalues is small the deduction of eigenvalues may well become impracticable. On the other hand, it may be sufficient to derive the distribution of eigenvalues, that is the number of solutions of the characteristic equation (corresponding to eigenvalues) between any two numerical limits. Distributions of this kind can be derived without solving the characteristic equation.

If a matrix is almost of diagonal form its diagonalization can be performed in algebraical terms by a method of successive approximation known as 'perturbation theory'. Let a Hermitean or unitary matrix have the form

$$\mathbf{C} = \mathbf{A} + \beta \mathbf{B} \tag{27.1}$$

where $\mathbf{A}$ is a diagonal matrix and β is a small parameter. It is attempted to obtain the diagonalized matrix $\mathbf{C}'$ and the unitary transformation matrix $\mathbf{U}$ in a series of ascending powers of β

$$\mathbf{C}' = \mathbf{A} + \beta \mathbf{D} + \beta^2 \mathbf{E} + \ldots \tag{27.2}$$

and

$$\mathbf{U} = \mathbf{I} + \beta \mathbf{V} + \beta^2 \mathbf{W} + \ldots \tag{27.3}$$

It is further assumed that all eigenvalues α_i of $\mathbf{A}$ are distinct from each other.

Expanding the equation

$$\mathbf{CU} = \mathbf{UC}'$$

in the form

$$\begin{aligned} &\mathbf{A} + \beta(\mathbf{B} + \mathbf{AV}) + \beta^2(\mathbf{AW} + \mathbf{BV}) + \ldots \\ &\quad = \mathbf{A} + \beta(\mathbf{VA} + \mathbf{D}) + \beta^2(\mathbf{WA} + \mathbf{VD} + \mathbf{E}) + \ldots \end{aligned} \tag{27.4}$$

the factors of every power of β are set equal to each other. As the first terms on either side cancel the equation to be solved first is

$$\mathbf{B} + \mathbf{AV} - \mathbf{VA} - \mathbf{D} = 0 \tag{27.5}$$

The diagonal element of this equation is

$$b_{jj} + \sum_k (a_{jk} v_{kj} - v_{jk} a_{kj}) - d_{jj} = 0$$

All terms in the sums vanish except $a_{jj} v_{jj} - v_{jj} a_{jj}$ which cancel; hence

$$d_{jj} = b_{jj} \tag{27.6}$$

The first order correction of the eigenvalues is accordingly equal to the diagonal elements of $\beta \mathbf{B}$.

The non-diagonal elements of (27.5) are related by

$$b_{jk} + \sum_m (a_{jm}v_{mk} - v_{jm}a_{mk}) - d_{jk} = 0$$

The last term vanishes and the sums reduce to two terms,

$$a_{jj}v_{jk} - v_{jk}a_{kk}$$

so that

$$v_{jk} = -\frac{b_{jk}}{a_{jj} - a_{kk}} \quad (j \neq k) \tag{27.7}$$

The elements v_{jj} remain undetermined; however, as $\mathbf{I} + \beta\mathbf{V}$ is to be unitary it is necessary that

$$(\mathbf{I} + \beta\mathbf{V})(\mathbf{I} + \beta\mathbf{V})^* = \mathbf{I} + \beta(\mathbf{V} + \mathbf{V}^*) + O(\beta^2) = \mathbf{I} + O(\beta^2)$$

Therefore the real part of v_{jj} must vanish. It is convenient to set $v_{jj} = 0$.

The next equation to be solved is

$$\mathbf{AW} + \mathbf{BV} - \mathbf{WA} - \mathbf{VD} - \mathbf{E} = 0 \tag{27.8}$$

Its diagonal element is

$$\sum_m (a_{jm}w_{mj} + b_{jm}v_{mj} - w_{jm}a_{mj} - v_{jm}d_{mj}) - e_{jj} = 0$$

Again most terms in the sums which involve the elements of the matrix $\mathbf{A}$ vanish; the sum involving $\mathbf{D}$ vanishes completely; thus

$$a_{jj}w_{jj} - w_{jj}a_{jj} + \sum_m b_{jm}v_{mj} - e_{jj} = 0$$

or, by (27.7),

$$e_{jj} = -\sum_m \frac{b_{jm}b_{mj}}{a_{mm} - a_{jj}} \tag{27.9}$$

If a_{jj} is the lowest eigenvalue of $\mathbf{A}$ and if $\mathbf{B}$ is Hermitean then e_{jj} must be negative.

Higher order corrections to the eigenvalues and eigenvectors can be derived by continuing this procedure but the expressions tend to become unwieldy.

If some of the eigenvalues are equal the method is not applicable in its present form as the denominators in (27.7) would vanish. It can nevertheless be applied to an eigenvalue which is different from the others. If a set of 2, 3 . . . s eigenvalues are equal to each other one can start by diagonalizing the 2, 3 . . . s dimensional sub-matrix in which these eigenvalues are contained. Subsequently the present method is applicable.

With these hints on practical diagonalization we conclude the presentation of matrix algebra and turn to its most important applications.

EXERCISES

1. Diagonalize the matrices (10.1).

2. Show that the matrix **A** can be diagonalized by the unitary transformation matrix **U**, where

$$\mathbf{A} = \begin{bmatrix} 5 & 2 & -1 \\ 2 & 5 & -1 \\ -1 & -1 & 8 \end{bmatrix} \quad \mathbf{U} = \begin{bmatrix} i/\sqrt{2} & 1/\sqrt{3} & 1/\sqrt{6} \\ -i/\sqrt{2} & 1/\sqrt{3} & 1/\sqrt{6} \\ 0 & 1/\sqrt{3} & -2/\sqrt{6} \end{bmatrix}$$

3. The matrix

$$\begin{bmatrix} 1 & 0 & 0 & 0 \\ 0 & 0 & 1 & 0 \\ 0 & 1 & 0 & 0 \\ 0 & 0 & 0 & -1 \end{bmatrix}$$

is Hermitean and unitary. Discuss the consequences.

CHAPTER 8

OSCILLATIONS

28. Simultaneous differential equations

Matrices are useful for solving systems of linear differential equations. Let $x_1, x_2 \ldots x_n$ be unknown functions of a single independent variable (t) and connected by simultaneous differential equations with constant coefficients:

$$\begin{aligned} dx_1/dt &= a_{11}x_1 + a_{12}x_2 + \ldots + a_{1n}x_n \\ dx_2/dt &= a_{21}x_1 + a_{22}x_2 + \ldots + a_{2n}x_n \\ &\vdots \\ dx_n/dt &= a_{n1}x_1 + a_{n2}x_2 + \ldots + a_{nn}x_n \end{aligned} \tag{28.1}$$

They can be written in terms of a vector and a matrix as

$$d\mathbf{x}/dt = \mathbf{A}\mathbf{x} \tag{28.2}$$

In solving this equation let $\mathbf{V}$ be a matrix independent of t and $\mathbf{y}$ another vector determined by

$$\mathbf{x} = \mathbf{V}\mathbf{y} \tag{28.3}$$

Substitution of (28.3) into (28.2) gives

$$\mathbf{V}(d\mathbf{y}/dt) = \mathbf{A}\mathbf{V}\mathbf{y} \tag{28.4}$$

It is now assumed that $\mathbf{A}$ can be diagonalized by a collineatory transformation so that

$$\mathbf{A}' = \mathbf{V}^{-1}\mathbf{A}\mathbf{V}$$

is a diagonal matrix. The transformed equation is resolved into components by

$$\begin{aligned} dy_1/dt &= \alpha_1 y_1 \\ &\vdots \\ dy_n/dt &= \alpha_n y_n \end{aligned} \tag{28.5}$$

These equations are readily integrated:

$$\begin{aligned} y_1 &= C_1 \exp(\alpha_1 t) \\ y_2 &= C_2 \exp(\alpha_2 t) \\ y_n &= C_n \exp(\alpha_n t) \end{aligned} \tag{28.6}$$

where $C_1 \ldots C_n$ are arbitrary constants and $\alpha_1 \ldots \alpha_n$ are the eigenvalues of $\mathbf{A}$. The corresponding eigenvectors are the columns of $\mathbf{V}$. If the matrix $\mathbf{A}$ is Hermitean the components of $\mathbf{y}$ are real exponential functions of t.

It is convenient to identify first the particular solutions of (28.1) in which all x_j are exponential functions of t. For this purpose one of the C_j is taken to be unity whereas the others are 0. In this way n different vectors are defined which have a single non-vanishing component varying exponentially with t. The transformation (28.3) yields:

$$x_k^{(j)} = v_{kj} \exp(\alpha_j t) \tag{28.7}$$

The general solutions of (28.1) are linear combinations of solutions of the type (28.7) with arbitrary coefficients.

Systems of simultaneous second order equations with constant coefficients can be solved in a similar way. The equation

$$d^2\mathbf{x}/dt^2 = \mathbf{A}\mathbf{x} \tag{28.8}$$

is transformed to

$$d^2\mathbf{y}/dt^2 = \mathbf{A}'\mathbf{y}$$

where

$$\mathbf{A}' = \mathbf{V}^{-1}\mathbf{A}\mathbf{V}$$

is a diagonal matrix; $\mathbf{V}$ and $\mathbf{y}$ are defined as before. Thus the original equations are transformed to

$$\begin{aligned} d^2y_1/dt^2 &= \alpha_1 y_1 \\ &\cdot \quad \cdot \\ &\cdot \quad \cdot \\ &\cdot \quad \cdot \\ d^2y_n/dt^2 &= \alpha_n y_n \end{aligned}$$

Integration results in

$$\begin{aligned} y_1 &= C_1 \exp(\alpha_1^{1/2} t) + D_1 \exp(-\alpha_1^{1/2} t) \\ &\cdot \qquad \cdot \qquad \cdot \\ &\cdot \qquad \cdot \qquad \cdot \\ &\cdot \qquad \cdot \qquad \cdot \\ y_n &= C_n \exp(\alpha_n^{1/2} t) + D_n \exp(-\alpha_n^{1/2} t) \end{aligned} \tag{28.9}$$

where $C_1 \ldots C_n$ and $D_1 \ldots D_n$ are arbitrary constants. If the eigenvalues of $\mathbf{A}$ are real and negative the solutions are periodic functions of t. It is again possible to identify those particular solutions in which all x_j depend exponentially upon t and the general solution is a linear combination of these particular solutions.

Application of matrices in solving simultaneous differential equations is made in theories of oscillations.

29. Oscillations of three particles in one dimension

Consider at first two particles of mass m interacting with conservative forces and constrained to move in a single dimension only. In the absence of any additional forces their equations of motion are

$$\begin{aligned} m\mathrm{d}^2(x_1 + x_2)/\mathrm{d}t^2 &= 0 \\ m\mathrm{d}^2(x_1 - x_2)/\mathrm{d}t^2 &= F(x_2 - x_1) \end{aligned} \tag{29.1}$$

where x_1 and x_2 are the coordinates of the particles, t is the time and F is the force depending on the distance between the particles. According to the first equation of (29.1) the centre of mass must stay at rest or move at constant speed. It is assumed that the forces of interaction tend to keep the particles at fixed distances apart (denoted by a) or to bring them back to these distances if they have been displaced:

$$F(x_1 - x_2) = -(x_1 - x_2 - a)k + \mathrm{O}(x_1 - x_2 - a)^2$$

where k is a positive constant. Denoting $x_1 - x_2 - a$ by x and neglecting the last term the second equation of (29.1) becomes

$$\frac{\mathrm{d}^2x}{\mathrm{d}t^2} = -\frac{k}{m}x$$

According to this equation the particles perform simple harmonic motion with frequency $\omega = (k/m)^{1/2}$.

Consider now three particles performing an oscillatory movement about some rectilinear configuration of equilibrium. It is convenient to specify their positions in terms of their displacements x_1, x_2 and x_3 from their positions of equilibrium. The forces of interaction are to act between nearest neighbours only and to be equal to

$$F_1 = -k(x_1 - x_2), \quad F_3 = -k(x_3 - x_2)$$
$$F_2 = -F_1 - F_3$$

(k being a positive constant) so that the interaction between particles 1 and 2 is the same as the interaction between particles 3 and 2.

It is further assumed that the masses of the particles 1 and 3 are equal to each other and differ from the mass of the particle 2. The masses are denoted by m and M respectively. The equations of motion are

$$\begin{aligned} m\mathrm{d}^2x_1/\mathrm{d}t^2 &= k(-x_1 + x_2) \\ M\mathrm{d}^2x_2/\mathrm{d}t^2 &= k(+x_1 - 2x_2 + x_3) \\ m\mathrm{d}^2x_3/\mathrm{d}t^2 &= k(x_2 - x_3) \end{aligned} \tag{29.2}$$

and can be solved by the method described in the preceding section.

First, new coordinates are defined as

$$s_1 = m^{1/2}x_1, \quad s_2 = M^{1/2}x_2, \quad s_3 = m^{1/2}x_3 \tag{29.3}$$

to be regarded as the components of a vector **s**. The equations of motion are transformed to

$$d^2\mathbf{s}/dt^2 = \mathbf{A}\mathbf{s} \tag{29.4}$$

where

$$\mathbf{A} = k\begin{bmatrix} -1/m & (1/mM)^{1/2} & 0 \\ (1/mM)^{1/2} & -2/M & (1/Mm)^{1/2} \\ 0 & (1/mM)^{1/2} & -1/m \end{bmatrix}$$

is a real symmetric matrix, so that it can be diagonalized by a unitary transformation. As a first step the characteristic equation

$$\begin{vmatrix} -(k/m) - \alpha & k/(Mm)^{1/2} & 0 \\ k/(mM)^{1/2} & -2(k/M) - \alpha & k/(Mm)^{1/2} \\ 0 & k/(Mm)^{1/2} & -(k/m) - \alpha \end{vmatrix} = 0$$

is expanded:

$$\alpha\left[\alpha^2 + 2\alpha k\left(\frac{1}{m} + \frac{1}{M}\right) + k^2\left(\frac{2}{Mm} + \frac{1}{m^2}\right)\right] = 0$$

The solutions are

$$\alpha_1 = 0; \quad \alpha_2 = -\frac{k}{m}; \quad \alpha_3 = -k\left(\frac{2}{M} + \frac{1}{m}\right)$$

The eigenvectors are derived by solving three sets of three simultaneous equations.

$$\begin{aligned} -\frac{1}{m}v_{11} + \left(\frac{1}{mM}\right)^{1/2} v_{21} &= 0 \\ \left(\frac{1}{mM}\right)^{1/2} v_{11} - \frac{2}{M}v_{21} + \left(\frac{1}{mM}\right)^{1/2} v_{31} &= 0 \\ \left(\frac{1}{mM}\right)^{1/2} v_{21} - \frac{1}{m}v_{31} &= 0 \end{aligned} \tag{29.5}$$

$$\begin{aligned} -\frac{1}{m}v_{12} + \left(\frac{1}{mM}\right)^{1/2} v_{22} &= -\frac{1}{m}v_{12} \\ \left(\frac{1}{mM}\right)^{1/2} v_{12} - \frac{2}{M}v_{22} + \left(\frac{1}{mM}\right)^{1/2} v_{32} &= -\frac{1}{m}v_{22} \\ \left(\frac{1}{mM}\right)^{1/2} v_{22} - \frac{1}{m}v_{32} &= -\frac{1}{m}v_{32} \end{aligned} \tag{29.6}$$

$$\begin{aligned} -\frac{1}{m}v_{13} + \left(\frac{1}{mM}\right)^{1/2} v_{23} &= -\left(\frac{2}{M} + \frac{1}{m}\right)v_{13} \\ \left(\frac{1}{mM}\right)^{1/2} v_{13} - \frac{2}{M}v_{23} + \left(\frac{1}{mM}\right)^{1/2} v_{33} &= -\left(\frac{2}{M} + \frac{1}{m}\right)v_{23} \\ \left(\frac{1}{mM}\right)^{1/2} v_{23} - \frac{1}{m}v_{33} &= -\left(\frac{2}{M} + \frac{1}{m}\right)v_{33} \end{aligned} \tag{29.7}$$

It is sufficient to solve two equations in each set of three; the third is redundant but does not involve any inconsistency. By solving the equations the ratios of two of the components to the third component are obtained; the components themselves are derived by normalization. If the eigenvectors are normalized and can be shown to be mutually orthogonal they are the columns of a unitary matrix **V** which is the transformation matrix of the matrix **A**. In this way the matrix **V** is constructed:

$$\mathbf{V} = \begin{bmatrix} 1/\nu_1 & 1/\nu_2 & 1/\nu_3 \\ (M/m\nu_1^2)^{1/2} & 0 & -2(m/M\nu_3^2)^{1/2} \\ 1/\nu_1 & -(1/\nu_2) & 1/\nu_3 \end{bmatrix}$$

where

$$\nu_1^2 = 2 + (M/m); \quad \nu_3^2 = 2 + 4(m/M); \quad \nu_2^2 = 2$$

It is readily verified that the three columns of **V** are mutually orthogonal.

By means of this transformation matrix equation (29.4) is transformed to

$$\mathrm{d}^2 y_j/\mathrm{d}t^2 = \alpha_j y_j$$

which is solved by

$$y_j = C_j \cos(\sqrt{(-\alpha_j)}t + \phi_j)$$

where C_j and ϕ_j are arbitrary real constants. We define three vectors by taking the constants $\phi_j = 0$ and letting C_j be successively 1, 0, 0; 0, 1, 0; 0, 0, 1.

As a result we obtain three 'modes of vibration' determining the synchronous movement of the three particles. They perform simple harmonic motion with real or zero frequencies (corresponding to the eigenvalues of **A** being negative or zero).

So far the modes of vibration are specified in terms of the components of **s**. By way of equation (29.3) they are converted to equations determining the time dependence of the displacements of the particles x_j. The result is:

$$\begin{aligned} x_1^{(1)} &= 1/\nu_1 = x_2^{(1)} = x_3^{(1)} \\ x_1^{(2)} &= (1/\nu_2)\cos[(k/m)^{1/2}t] = -x_3^{(2)} \\ x_2^{(2)} &= 0 \\ x_1^{(3)} &= (1/\nu_3)\cos\{[(2k/M) + (k/m)]^{1/2}t\} = x_3^{(3)} \\ x_2^{(3)} &= -2(m/M)x_1^{(3)} \end{aligned} \qquad (29.8)$$

The first mode consists of a translation of the three particles at uniform velocity (corresponding to zero frequency). The two other modes are oscillations proper. In the second mode the central particle stays at rest whereas the two other particles move at equal amplitudes and opposite phases. In the third mode the first and third particle have equal amplitudes and phases; the second particle has opposite phase and a different (usually larger) amplitude. The general solution of the equations of motion is a superposition of these modes with arbitrary phases and amplitudes.

The present theory is readily generalized so that it applies to chains of four, five and more particles. The solution of the characteristic equation is, however, no longer possible by elementary methods and the other steps in the mathematical deduction become more and more cumbersome. If, however, the number of particles is very large the theory can again be simplified. This will be considered in the following section.

30. Linear chains

Consider a chain of particles oscillating about a configuration of equilibrium in which the 'links' of the chain have a fixed length. Forces acting along the links tend to restore their lengths to the value at equilibrium. If the particles are labelled 1 to N the force on the jth particle is equal to

$$k(x_{j-1} - 2x_j + x_{j+1})$$

where the positive constant k is the same for all triplets of particles.

Provided that the number of particles is very large it is plausible to assume that the movement of the two particles at the ends of the chain will virtually not affect the movement of the remaining $N-2$ particles. The theory can be simplified by letting the particles at the ends be subject to a constraint known as a 'periodic boundary condition'. The meaning of this constraint is explained by placing an additional particle at the left end and an additional particle at the right end of the chain. The constraint is of such a kind that the additional particle at the left end is to move precisely in phase with the particle N; also the additional particle at the right end is to move precisely in phase with the particle 1. The periodic boundary condition is readily taken into account by assuming that the particle N interacts with the particle 1 as if they were nearest neighbours.

With these assumptions the equations of motion of the chain are

$$m(\mathrm{d}^2x_j/\mathrm{d}t^2) = k(x_{j-1} - 2x_j + x_{j+1}) \tag{30.1}$$

where $j = 1, 2 \ldots N$ $(x_{N+1} = x_1; x_0 = x_N)$, and where m is the mass of the particles. In matrix and vector notation these equations are represented by

$$\mathrm{d}^2\mathbf{x}/\mathrm{d}t^2 = \mathbf{A}\mathbf{x} \tag{30.2}$$

The elements of the matrix $\mathbf{A}$ are zero except for

$$a_{jj} = -2k/m; \quad a_{j(j+1)} = a_{j(j-1)} = k/m \tag{30.3}$$

The elements a_{1N} and a_{N1} are equal to k/m.

On account of the periodic boundary condition the chain has acquired an important symmetry property. If it moves in such a way that the particle N takes the place of 1, the particle 1 takes the place of 2, the particle $N - 1$ takes the place of particle N with all intermediate particles moving up by one link, the set of equations (30.1) remains unchanged. On account of this it is possible to identify the eigenvectors of the matrix **A** without having any knowledge of the eigenvalues.

The above shift to the right is mathematically specified by a matrix **T** with the elements $t_{j(j+1)} = 1$ (including $t_{N1} = 1$) whereas all other elements t_{jk} vanish. Thus, if

$$\mathbf{x}' = \mathbf{T}\mathbf{x}$$

then

$$x_j = x_{j-1}$$

It will now be shown that the matrices **A** and **T** commute. Let $\mathbf{S} = \mathbf{TA} - \mathbf{AT}$, so that

$$s_{jk} = \sum_l (t_{jl}a_{lk} - a_{jl}t_{lk}) = t_{j(j+1)}a_{(j+1)k} - a_{j(k-1)}t_{(k-1)k}$$

$$= a_{(j+1)k} - a_{j(k-1)}$$

Hence

$$s_{(j-1)k} = a_{jk} - a_{(j-1)(k-1)}$$

On account of (30.3) it is merely necessary to consider those elements of **S** which depend on the elements of **A** in the leading diagonal or in a diagonal adjacent to it. They are

$$s_{(j-1)(j-1)} = a_{j(j-1)} - a_{(j-1)(j-2)} = 1 - 1 = 0$$

$$s_{(j-1)j} = a_{jj} - a_{(j-1)(j-1)} = -2 - (-2) = 0$$

$$s_{(j-1)(j+1)} = a_{j(j+1)} - a_{(j-1)j} = 1 - 1 = 0$$

Hence all elements of **S** vanish so that

$$\mathbf{TA} - \mathbf{AT} = 0 \tag{30.4}$$

The eigenvectors of **A** are determined by

$$\mathbf{Av} = \alpha\mathbf{v}$$

Multiplication by **T** gives

$$\mathbf{TAv} = \mathbf{ATv} = \alpha\mathbf{Tv} \tag{30.5}$$

so that **Tv** is also an eigenvector. If a normalized eigenvector is multiplied by $e^{i\chi}$ where χ is a real number it still remains a normalized eigenvector. It follows then from (30.5) that

$$\mathbf{Tv} = \mathbf{v}\,e^{i\chi} \tag{30.6}$$

It follows also that the eigenvectors of **A** are also eigenvectors of **T**. In order that equation (30.6) should be valid it is necessary to prove that the eigenvalues of **A** are non-degenerate or at least, to show that the number of eigenvectors derived from (30.6) is equal to N. This will be shown in due course.

In order to comply with equation (30.6) and simultaneously with

$$(\mathbf{Tv})_j = v_{j+1}$$

the eigenvector $\mathbf{v}_{\cdot n}$ must have the components

$$v_{1n}, \quad v_{1n} \exp(\mathrm{i}\chi_n), \quad v_{1n} \exp(2\mathrm{i}\chi_n) \ldots v_{1n} \exp(N\mathrm{i}\chi_n)$$

Further, if this vector is to be normalized it is necessary to put $v_{1n} = N^{-1/2}$.

The phase constants χ are found by remembering that $\mathbf{T}^2, \mathbf{T}^3 \ldots \mathbf{T}^N$ have the effect of moving the chain 2, 3 . . . N links respectively to the right. But the last operation restores the original position of the chain. Therefore it is necessary that

$$\mathbf{T}^N\mathbf{v} = \mathbf{v}, \quad \mathbf{T}^N = \mathbf{I}$$

χ_n must accordingly be an Nth root of unity and

$$N\chi_n = 2\pi n, \quad \chi_n = 2\pi n/N$$

where n may be any integer between 1 and N. In this way N independent eigenvectors of χ are identified and on account of this result the validity of the procedure is justified.

Let $\mathbf{V}$ be a unitary matrix diagonalizing $\mathbf{A}$ and independent of the time. The elements of $\mathbf{V}$ are accordingly

$$v_{jn} = (N)^{-1/2} \, \mathrm{e}^{2\pi \mathrm{i} nj/N} \tag{30.7}$$

The verification of the orthogonality of the columns of $\mathbf{V}$ is left to the reader as an exercise. It may be pointed out that the identification of the eigenvectors is entirely independent of k and the mass of the particles.

The eigenvalues of $\mathbf{A}$ are found by substituting the expressions (30.7) into the equation

$$\mathbf{A}\mathbf{v}_{\cdot n} = \alpha_n \mathbf{v}_{\cdot n}$$

In terms of components this is

$$\alpha_n v_{ln} = \sum_j a_{lj} v_{jn} = N^{-1/2}(a_{l(l-1)} v_{(l-1)n} + a_{ll} v_{ln} + a_{l(l+1)} v_{(l+1)n})$$

By (30.3) and (30.7)

$$\alpha_n N^{-1/2} \exp\left(\frac{2\pi \mathrm{i} nl}{N}\right) = N^{-1/2} \exp\left(\frac{2\pi \mathrm{i} nl}{N}\right)\left(\frac{k}{m}\right)$$
$$\left[-2 + \exp\left(-\frac{2\pi \mathrm{i} n}{N}\right) + \exp\left(\frac{2\pi \mathrm{i} n}{N}\right)\right]$$

The expression in the square bracket is equal to

$$2\left[\cos\left(\frac{2\pi n}{N}\right) - 1\right] = -4 \sin^2\left(\frac{\pi n}{N}\right)$$

Hence the eigenvalues are

$$\alpha_n = \frac{-4k}{m} \sin^2\left(\frac{\pi n}{N}\right) \tag{30.8}$$

They are negative and their magnitudes are of the order of the square of the frequency for an isolated pair of particles.

The modes of vibration are specified by

$$\mathbf{x}^{(n)} = \mathbf{v}_{\cdot k} \exp(t\alpha_n^{1/2})$$

They represent a type of movement in which all particles of the chain oscillate synchronously with their amplitudes periodically returning to the same value after N/n links of the chain. The modes are very similar to the standing waves of acoustics.

This deduction of the frequencies of a chain shows that the solution of the characteristic equation can be avoided if the system is symmetric enough.

Consider now a chain where the links have two different lengths which alternate regularly. The force constants also have two alternating values. The equations of motion for a chain of $2N$ particles are now

$$\begin{aligned} m\mathrm{d}^2x_{2j}/\mathrm{d}t^2 &= Kx_{2j-1} - (k+K)x_{2j} + kx_{2j+1} \\ m\mathrm{d}^2x_{2j+1}/\mathrm{d}t^2 &= kx_{2j} - (k+K)x_{2j+1} + Kx_{2j+2} \end{aligned} \tag{30.9}$$

where k and K are the force constants and $j = 1, 2 \ldots N$. The periodic boundary condition is taken into account by defining $x_{2N+1} = x_1$ and $x_0 = x_{2N}$. The equations are of the form (30.2) if $\mathbf{A}$ is a matrix of $2N$ rows and columns and

$$\begin{aligned} a_{2j,\,2j} &= a_{(2j+1)(2j+1)} = -(k+K)/m \\ a_{(2j-1)2j} &= a_{2j(2j-1)} = K/m \\ a_{(2j+1)2j} &= a_{2j(2j+1)} = k/m \quad (j = 1 \ldots N) \end{aligned} \tag{30.10}$$

By the same arguments as before the components of the eigenvectors can be identified, but not completely. There are two components associated with every value of j:

$$\begin{aligned} v_{2j\ n} &= p(\tfrac{1}{2}N)^{1/2} \exp\left(\frac{2\pi i n j}{N}\right) \\ v_{(2j+1)n} &= q(\tfrac{1}{2}N)^{1/2} \exp\left[\frac{2\pi i n(j+1/2)}{N}\right] \end{aligned}$$

where n may have the values $1 \ldots N$ and p and q are independent of j but otherwise undetermined. To find the eigenvalues one solves

$$\mathbf{A}\mathbf{v}_{\cdot n} = \alpha_n \mathbf{v}_{\cdot n}$$

and the following set of equations is obtained:

$$-p[k+K+\alpha_n]+q\left[K\exp\left(\frac{-\mathrm{i}\pi n}{N}\right)+k\exp\left(\frac{\mathrm{i}\pi n}{N}\right)\right]=0$$
$$p\left[k\exp\left(\frac{-\mathrm{i}\pi n}{N}\right)+K\exp\left(\frac{\mathrm{i}\pi n}{N}\right)\right]-q[k+K+\alpha_n]=0 \qquad (30.11)$$

In these equations a common factor $(\frac{1}{2}N)^{1/2}\exp(2\pi inj/N)$ has been divided out; the resulting equations (30.11) are independent of j. In order to solve them it is necessary to diagonalize the Hermitean matrix

$$\begin{bmatrix} -(k+K) & \left[K\exp\left(\frac{-\mathrm{i}\pi n}{N}\right)+k\exp\left(\frac{\mathrm{i}\pi n}{N}\right)\right] \\ \left[k\exp\left(\frac{\mathrm{i}\pi n}{N}\right)+K\exp\left(\frac{\mathrm{i}\pi n}{N}\right)\right] & -(k+K) \end{bmatrix}$$

Thus the eigenvalues of this matrix are the same as the eigenvalues of $\mathbf{A}$ and equal to

$$\alpha_n=\left(\frac{1}{m}\right)\left\{-(k+K)\pm\left[K^2+k^2+2kK\cos\left(\frac{2\pi n}{N}\right)\right]^{1/2}\right\} \qquad (30.12)$$

Every value of n corresponds therefore to two eigenvalues. They are all either larger or smaller than $-(k+K)$. Thus the natural frequencies of the chain have two sets of modes the frequencies of which are separated by a finite gap.

A similar result is obtained for linear chains in which the force constants are uniform but the masses of the particles have two alternating values.

The chains considered in this section can be regarded as one dimensional models for a monatomic crystal, for a crystal of diatomic molecules and for a lattice consisting of two kinds of ions. In the latter case the two types of modes are the 'acoustic' and 'optical' oscillations of the lattice. As far as the diatomic molecules are concerned the two branches do not admit such a simple interpretation but might be roughly described as intermolecular and intramolecular oscillations.

It can be noted that the mechanical oscillations of chains of particles are closely analogous to certain types of electric oscillations in communication lines. Consider as an example a number of coils in series, with a lead to earth, via a condenser, between every pair of coils. A line of this sort can perform electrical oscillations which are not too heavily damped. If the coils have equal inductances and the condensers equal capacities, the natural frequencies of the line are approximately defined by an equation of the form (30.8). In this case the line admits low-frequency oscillations, filtering out frequencies higher than a finite limit. If the two kinds of alternating condensers are used the line admits two separated bands of frequencies.

31. Disordered chains

If the masses of the particles or the force constants in the links of a chain are not uniform but distributed at random the high symmetry of the chain is lost and the methods of Section 30 are no longer applicable. In fact there is no general method for deriving the frequencies of the modes of vibration. A certain amount of insight into the dynamics of the chain can still be obtained from the spectral distribution, that is the number of modes within given intervals of frequencies.

In this section a deduction of this distribution is given; it will be noted that even this limited result requires a greater mathematical effort than the complete dynamics of regular chains.

The equations of motion are of the form (29.4) if the elements of the matrix **A** are

$$\begin{aligned} a_{jj} &= -[k_{j(j-1)} + k_{j(j+1)}](m_j)^{-1} \equiv a_j \\ a_{j(j-1)} = a_{(j-1)j} &= k_{j(j-1)}(m_j m_{j-1})^{-1/2} \equiv b_j \end{aligned} \qquad (31.1)$$

The masses m_j and the force constants $k_{j(j-1)} = k_{(j-1)j}$ are arbitrary positive numbers. It is not attempted to invoke the periodic boundary condition. All matrix elements outside the leading diagonal and the two adjacent diagonals are zero.

The eigenvalues of **A** are real and it is assumed that they are negative; the movement of the chain then consists of stable oscillations. The negative squares of their circular frequencies are equal to the eigenvalues of **A**.

The number of modes where the square of the frequency is equal to or smaller than an arbitrary number μ is a positive integer not larger than N. If N is large enough this number can be replaced by a continuous function of μ which will be denoted by $\int_0^\mu D(\mu)\,\mathrm{d}\mu$. The function under the integral sign is the distribution function of the modes on the frequency scale; $D(\mu)\,\mathrm{d}\mu$ is the number of modes in the infinitesimal interval of frequencies between μ and $\mu + \mathrm{d}\mu$. By definition,

$$\int_0^\infty D(\mu)\,\mathrm{d}\mu = N \qquad (31.2)$$

In attempting to derive an expression for the function $D(\mu)$ in terms of the matrix elements an indirect approach is required. It involves the introduction of auxiliary quantities which do not admit any direct physical interpretation.

In the first instance consider the matrix

$$\mathbf{P} = -\mathbf{A} + \lambda\mathbf{I} \tag{31.3}$$

where λ is a parameter and $\mathbf{I}$ the unit matrix. Let the negative eigenvalues of $\mathbf{A}$ be denoted by μ_l which are, accordingly, positive numbers.

Then

$$\det \mathbf{P} = \prod_{l=1}^{N} (\mu_l + \lambda^{-1})$$

and

$$\log \det \mathbf{P} = \sum_l \log [\mu_l + (1/\lambda)]$$

In accordance with the assumed continuity of $D(\mu)$ the last sum is replaced by an integral

$$\log \det \mathbf{P} = \int_0^\infty \log [\mu + (1/\lambda)] D(\mu)\, d\mu \tag{31.4}$$

The left-hand side of this equation is a function of the parameter λ and can be regarded as a 'transform' of the distribution function $D(\mu)$, comparable with Fourier or Laplace transforms. If the left-hand side can be expressed in terms of the matrix elements of $\mathbf{A}$ and if the transformation can be inverted we have an explicit solution of the problem under consideration.

As a next step in this direction the determinant on the left-hand side is scrutinized. Let $\mathbf{P}^{(j)}$ be the sub-matrix consisting of the rows and columns of $\lambda\mathbf{P}$ which are labelled as $j, j+1, j+2 \ldots N$, so that the larger values of j correspond to the smaller numbers of dimensions.

$$\mathbf{P}^{(j)} = \begin{bmatrix} \lambda a_j + 1 & \lambda b_j & & & \\ \lambda b_j & \lambda a_{j+1} + 1 & \lambda b_{j+2} & & \\ & & \lambda b_{N-3} & \lambda a_{N-1} + 1 & \lambda b_{N-1} \\ & & & \lambda b_{N-1} & \lambda a_N + 1 \end{bmatrix}$$

According to the definition

$$\det \mathbf{P}^{(1)} = \det (\lambda\mathbf{P}) = \lambda^N \det \mathbf{P} \tag{31.5}$$

the expansion of $\det \mathbf{P}^{(j)}$ according to (13.1) consists of two terms

$$\det \mathbf{P}^{(j)} = (\lambda a_j + 1)\mathbf{P}^{(j+1)} - \lambda^2 b_j^2 \mathbf{P}^{(j+2)} \tag{31.6}$$

(31.6) can be used as a recurrence formula, by expressing the determinants in terms of

$$\begin{aligned} \det \mathbf{P}^{(N)} &= \lambda a_N + 1 \\ \det \mathbf{P}^{(N-1)} &= (\lambda a_N + 1)(\lambda a_{N-1} + 1) - \lambda^2 b_{N-1}^2 \end{aligned} \tag{31.7}$$

These determinants can be related to certain continued fractions to be denoted by f_j where j can have the values $1 \ldots N$. They are defined by

$$f_j = 1 + \lambda a_j - [\lambda^2 b_j^2/[1 + \lambda a_{j+1} - \lambda^2 b_{j+1}^2/[1 + \lambda a_{j+2} - \lambda^2 b_{j+2}^2/\ldots \quad (31.8)$$

the last denominator being equal to $1 + \lambda a_N$. These fractions satisfy the recurrence formula

$$f_j = 1 + \lambda a_j - \frac{\lambda^2 b_j^2}{f_{j+1}} \quad (31.9)$$

and this is supplemented by

$$f_N = 1 + \lambda a_N \quad (31.10)$$

$$f_{N-1} = 1 + \lambda a_{N-1} - \frac{\lambda^2 b_{N-1}^2}{(1 + \lambda a_N)}$$

According to (31.10) and (31.7)

$$\det \mathbf{P}^{(N)} = f_N; \quad \det \mathbf{P}^{(N-1)} = f_{n-1} \det \mathbf{P}^{(N)} \quad (31.11)$$

If there is any value of j for which

$$\det \mathbf{P}^{(j-1)} = f_{j-1} \det \mathbf{P}^{(j)} \quad (31.12)$$

it follows from (31.6) that

$$\begin{aligned}\det \mathbf{P}^{(j-2)} &= (\lambda a_{j-2} + 1) \det \mathbf{P}^{(j-1)} - \lambda^2 b_{j-2}^2 \det \mathbf{P}^{(j)} \\ &= [(\lambda a_{j-2} + 1) f_{j-1} - \lambda^2 b_{j-2}^2] \det \mathbf{P}^{(j)}\end{aligned}$$

and by (31.9)

$$\det \mathbf{P}^{(j-2)} = f_{j-2} f_{j-1} \det \mathbf{P}^{(j)} \quad (31.13)$$

By (31.11) equation (31.12) is valid for $j = N$ and by (31.13) it follows that

$$\det \mathbf{P}^{(N-2)} = f_{N-2} f_{N-1} f_N$$

$$\det \mathbf{P}^{(j)} = \prod_{l=j}^{N} f_l$$

and, by (31.5)

$$\det \mathbf{P} = \lambda^{-N} \prod_{j=1}^{N} f_j \quad (31.14)$$

The left-hand side of (31.4) is accordingly

$$\log \det \mathbf{P} = -Nw + \sum_j \log f_j \quad (31.15)$$

where

$$w = \log \lambda \quad (31.16)$$

Thus the left-hand side of (31.4) is expressed in terms of the matrix elements a_{jk}. Finally it is necessary to express the function $D(\mu)$ in terms of the left-hand side of (31.4).

The right-hand side of (31.4) can be expressed in terms of a function of w denoted by $\Omega(w)$ and defined by the equation

$$-Nw + \int_0^\infty \log[\mu\, e^w + 1] D(\mu)\, d\mu = -Nw + \Omega(w)$$
$$= -Nw + \sum_j \log f_j \qquad (31.17)$$

and thus

$$d\Omega/dw = e^w \int_0^\infty \mu D(\mu)[1 + \mu\, e^w]^{-1}\, d\mu \qquad (31.18)$$

In order to express the left-hand side of this equation in terms of the function in the integrand another auxiliary quantity is required and defined as

$$R(q) = \int_{-\infty}^{\infty} (d\Omega/dw) \exp[-w(\tfrac{1}{2} + iq)]\, dw \qquad (31.19)$$

By (31.18)

$$R(q) = \int_{-\infty}^{\infty} \exp(\tfrac{1}{2}w - iqw)\left[\int_0^\infty \mu\, D(\mu)[1 + \mu\, e^w]^{-1}\, d\mu\right] dw$$

Rearranging the second integrand gives

$$\exp(\tfrac{1}{2}w)\exp(-iqw)[1 + \exp(w + \log\mu)]^{-1}$$
$$= [1 + e^z]^{-1}\{\exp[\tfrac{1}{2}(z - \log\mu)]\}[\exp(-iqz + iq\log\mu)]$$

where $z = w + \log\mu$. It follows that

$$R(q) = \int_0^\infty \mu^{1/2} D(\mu)\, e^{iq\log\mu}\, d\mu \int_{-\infty}^{\infty} \frac{e^{-iqz}}{2\cosh\frac{1}{2}z}\, dz$$

The last integral is the Fourier transform of $1/2\cosh\frac{1}{2}z$. It can be evaluated by contour integration. The contour consists of the real axis, a semicircle at infinity below the real axis and a set of small circles about the poles along the negative imaginary axis. The integral is reduced to a sum of residues arising from these poles and summation results in $\pi/\cosh\pi q$. The auxiliary function R is in this way related to the distribution function $D(\mu)$ by a Fourier transformation.

$$(2\pi^3)^{-1/2}(\cosh\pi q)R(q) = (2\pi)^{-1/2}\int_{-\infty}^{\infty} \mu^{3/2} D(\mu)\, e^{iq\log\mu}\, d(\log\mu)$$

The distribution function is accordingly found by Fourier inversion

$$D(\mu) = (1/2\pi^2)\int_{-\infty}^{\infty} (\cosh\pi q)R(q)\, e^{-iq\log\mu}\, dq \qquad (31.20)$$

This equation together with (31.19), (31.18) and (31.17) determines $D(\mu)$ in terms of the matrix elements a_{jk} which are the coefficients in the equations of motion. The integrals (31.19) and (31.20) converge sufficiently to admit numerical integration. Nevertheless the procedure is cumbersome. The result can be used if the matrix elements of **A** are determined only by way of some probability distribution. The statistical expectation of $D(\mu)$ is easier to evaluate than the distribution function itself.

The argument in the present section is characteristic for the peculiar problems arising if solid state theories are applied to disordered structures such as liquids.

32. Rectilinear molecules

Oscillations in three dimensions are in principle fully determined by the same theory which was applied to movement in a single dimension. In particular, if the masses and force constants are given, modes of vibration can be identified and the frequencies calculated. In practice calculations rapidly increase in complexity if the number of dimensions is increased.

The main field in which the theory can be applied is the oscillations of molecules; the results can frequently be tested by interpreting optical, infra-red and Raman spectra.

In this section the oscillations are considered of triatomic molecules which have a rectilinear shape in equilibrium and in which the outer atoms are of the same kind. The most important examples for this are carbon dioxide and carbon disulphide. A simplified theory of these oscillations has been given in Section 29; in a more exact calculation such as that given here it is necessary to consider the interaction of the two outer atoms and to allow for movement in three dimensions.

The instantaneous position of the three atoms is specified by nine displacements and there are nine components of the restoring forces. As in the previous case it will be assumed that every force component is a linear function of all the displacement components. They are accordingly elements of a nine-by-nine matrix **B** with eighty-one elements of which forty-five are independent. Simple, or at least manageable, results can be expected only if, on account of the symmetry of the molecule, the number of independent matrix elements is reduced.

In one dimension restoring forces are antiparallel to the displacement by which they are generated. In three dimensions in general it is possible that displacements generate forces perpendicular to their own direction. If, however, the molecule is rectilinear and the axis of the molecule is an axis of cylindrical symmetry it is not possible that an axial displacement gives rise to a force perpendicular to the axis, and the restoring forces are antiparallel to the displacement.

Let the equilibrium positions of the atoms be aligned along the

x axis, and let the components of the displacements be denoted by $x_1, y_1, z_1; x_2, y_2, z_2; x_3, y_3, z_3$. The x component of the restoring forces can then depend on x_1, x_2 and x_3 but on no other components of displacement. Similarly the y and z components of the forces can depend only on the y and z components of the displacements respectively. For this reason the equations of motion can be formulated for the x, y and z directions independently.

$$\begin{aligned} m\mathrm{d}^2x_1/\mathrm{d}t^2 &= b_{11}x_1 + b_{12}x_2 + b_{13}x_3 \\ M\mathrm{d}^2x_2/\mathrm{d}t^2 &= b_{12}x_1 + b_{22}x_2 + b_{23}x_3 \\ m\mathrm{d}^2x_3/\mathrm{d}t^2 &= b_{13}x_1 + b_{23}x_2 + b_{33}x_3 \end{aligned} \tag{32.1}$$

$$\begin{aligned} m\mathrm{d}^2y_1/\mathrm{d}t^2 &= b_{44}y_1 + b_{45}y_2 + b_{46}y_3 \\ M\mathrm{d}^2y_2/\mathrm{d}t^2 &= b_{45}y_1 + b_{55}y_2 + b_{56}y_3 \\ m\mathrm{d}^2y_3/\mathrm{d}t^2 &= b_{46}y_1 + b_{56}y_2 + b_{66}y_3 \end{aligned} \tag{32.2}$$

$$\begin{aligned} m\mathrm{d}^2z_1/\mathrm{d}t^2 &= b_{77}z_1 + b_{78}z_2 + b_{79}z_3 \\ M\mathrm{d}^2z_2/\mathrm{d}t^2 &= b_{78}z_1 + b_{88}z_2 + b_{89}z_3 \\ m\mathrm{d}^2z_3/\mathrm{d}t^2 &= b_{79}z_1 + b_{89}z_2 + b_{99}z_3 \end{aligned} \tag{32.3}$$

In these equations M is the mass of the atom labelled 2 and m is the mass of the atoms labelled 1 and 3. The matrix elements b_{jk} determine the restoring forces. Instead of the possible number of forty-five there are only eighteen independent matrix elements and the nine-by-nine matrix has been reduced to three three-by-three matrices.

On account of the cylindrical symmetry of the molecule the matrices in equations (32.2) and (32.3) must be equal to each other. In this way the number of independent constants is reduced to twelve. As the atoms 1 and 3 are supposed to be of the same kind further simplifications arise:

$$b_{11} = b_{33}; \quad b_{12} = b_{23}; \quad b_{44} = b_{66}; \quad b_{45} = b_{56} \tag{32.4}$$

As all forces in the molecule are internal forces they cannot give rise to any resultant force on the centre of mass or to a couple acting on the whole molecule. For these reasons the matrix elements b_{jk} are subject to additional restrictions.

The resultant force has the components

$$F_x = (b_{11} + b_{12} + b_{13})x_1 + (b_{12} + b_{22} + b_{23})x_2 + (b_{13} + b_{23} + b_{33})x_3 \tag{32.5}$$

$$F_y = (b_{44} + b_{45} + b_{46})y_1 + (b_{45} + b_{55} + b_{56})y_2 + (b_{46} + b_{56} + b_{66})y_3 \tag{32.6}$$

F_z is determined by an equation of the form (32.6) with the z components of displacement substituted for the y components.

In obtaining expressions for the components of the resultant couple the moment of the forces with respect to the centre of mass is taken. The centre of mass is, in the present example, in the position of the atom 2. The x component of the couple vanishes since the atoms are regarded as extensionless mass points. If the distance between neighbouring atoms in their equilibrium positions is denoted by D, the z component of the couple is equal to

$$0 = C_z = D[(b_{44} - b_{46})y_1 + (b_{45} - b_{56})y_2 + (b_{46} - b_{66})y_3] \quad (32.7)$$

A similar expression determines the component C_y with the z components of displacements substituted for the y components in (32.7)

The conditions $F_x = F_y = 0$, $C_z = 0$ are satisfied by setting every coefficient of the displacements in (32.5) (32.6) and (32.7) equal to zero. Hence

$$\begin{array}{ll} b_{11} + b_{12} + b_{13} = 0 & b_{44} + b_{45} + b_{56} = 0 \\ b_{12} + b_{22} + b_{23} = 0 & b_{45} + b_{55} + b_{56} = 0 \\ b_{13} + b_{23} + b_{33} = 0 & b_{46} + b_{56} + b_{66} = 0 \end{array}$$

$$\begin{array}{l} b_{44} - b_{46} = 0 \\ b_{45} - b_{56} = 0 \\ b_{46} - b_{66} = 0 \end{array} \quad (32.8)$$

Not all of these additional restrictions are independent of each other. A matrix in which all elements comply with the above conditions can be expressed in terms of three positive constants, to be denoted by f, g and h. A matrix similar to $\mathbf{B}$ and expressible in terms of these three constants and m and M, enters into the equations of motion which are of the form (29.4) with

$$\begin{array}{lll} s_1 = m^{-1/2}x_1 & s_2 = M^{-1/2}x_2 & s_3 = m^{-1/2}x_3 \\ s_4 = m^{-1/2}y_1 & s_5 = M^{-1/2}y_2 & s_6 = m^{-1/2}y_3 \\ s_7 = m^{-1/2}z_1 & s_8 = M^{-1/2}z_2 & s_9 = m^{-1/2}z_3 \end{array}$$

The matrix $\mathbf{A}$ consists of three sub-matrices in the rows and columns 1–3, 4–6 and 7–9 respectively and denoted by $\mathbf{A}_x$, $\mathbf{A}_y$ and $\mathbf{A}_z$. We have

$$\mathbf{A}_x = \begin{bmatrix} -f/m & g/(mM)^{1/2} & (f-g)/m \\ g/(mM)^{1/2} & -2g/M & g/(mM)^{1/2} \\ (f-g)/m & g/(mM)^{1/2} & -f/m \end{bmatrix}$$

$$\mathbf{A}_y = \mathbf{A}_z = \begin{bmatrix} -h/m & h/2(mM)^{1/2} & -h/m \\ h/2(mM)^{1/2} & -h/m & h/2(mM)^{1/2} \\ -h/m & h/2(mM)^{1/2} & -h/m \end{bmatrix} \quad (32.9)$$

Diagonalization of the matrix $\mathbf{A}_x$ leads to a result not very different from that of Section 29. The eigenvalues are

$$\alpha_1 = 0; \quad \left.\begin{matrix}\alpha_2\\ \alpha_3\end{matrix}\right\} = -\left(\frac{f}{m}+\frac{g}{m}\right) \pm \left[\left(\frac{f}{m}-\frac{g}{M}\right)^2 + \left(\frac{g}{m}\right)\left(\frac{g}{m}+\frac{2g}{M}-\frac{2f}{m}\right)\right]^{1/2} \quad (32.10)$$

The characteristic equation of the matrix $\mathbf{A}_y$ and $\mathbf{A}_z$ is

$$\alpha^3 + \alpha^2 h[(2/M) + (1/m)] = 0$$

and has the solutions

$$\alpha_4 = \alpha_5 = \alpha_7 = \alpha_8 = 0; \quad \alpha_6 = \alpha_9 = -h[(2/M) + (1/m)] \quad (32.11)$$

Zero frequencies are associated with uniform displacements of all atoms in three directions and to rotations of the molecule about the y and z directions. Results differ from those of the simplified theory by the emergence of three rather than two different frequencies of oscillations one of which is twofold degenerate. The new frequency $|\alpha_6|^{1/2}$ corresponds to a parallel movement of the atoms 1 and 3 conjointly with an antiparallel movement of the particle 2 perpendicular to the axis of the molecule.

The theory can be applied to the oscillations of the CO_2 and the CS_2 molecules. Three different fundamental frequencies have been identified in the infra-red and Raman spectra. Denoting the frequencies by ω_2, ω_3 and ω_6 and by applying equations (32.10) and (32.11) the constants f, g, h can be obtained in terms of the frequencies and the masses.

$$f = \frac{m(\omega_2^2+\omega_3^2)}{2[2+(M/m)]}\left[\left(1+\frac{M}{m}\right) \pm \left(1 - \frac{4\omega_2^2\omega_3^2}{(\omega_2^2+\omega_3^2)}\right)\right] \quad (32.12)$$

$$g = \tfrac{1}{2}M(\omega_2^2+\omega_3^2) - (M/m)f$$

$$h = 4\pi^2\omega_6^2[(2/M) + (1/m)]$$

The ambiguity in the first equation is not serious. If the forces between the atoms 1 and 3 are neglected this must restore the validity of the simplified theory of Section 29. Then $g = f$; which is possible only if the negative sign is adopted.

In the following table the experimental masses and frequencies

	M	m	ω_2	ω_3	ω_6	f	g	h
	10^{-24} g		10^{13} sec^{-1}			10^6 dyn cm^{-1}		
CO_2	19·94	26·56	25·6	44·2	12·5	1·55	1·43	0·114
CS_2	19·94	52·32	12·35	28·7	7·49	0·747	0·692	0·047

and the calculated force constants are shown. In order to render the experimental test of the theory complete it would be necessary to find values for the force constants in an independent way, for instance by theoretical deduction. So far it can only be said that their order of magnitude fits well to the force constants derived from the spectra of diatomic molecules.

33. Oscillations in three dimensions

If the equilibrium configuration of a molecule is not rectilinear the mathematics becomes increasingly cumbersome although the method of the preceding sections remains applicable. These aspects of the theory which are of general applicability are nevertheless worth considering; by their use the natural frequencies of specific molecules can be deduced to the extent that the necessary computations can be performed numerically by automatic computers.

The theory is simplified if the equilibrium configuration of the molecule has a high degree of symmetry. Whereas this symmetry is usually reduced by the movement of the atoms the time average over the period of a mode of vibration has the full symmetry. On account of this it is sometimes possible to identify modes of vibration without solving the characteristic equation, or at least to reduce the order of the characteristic equation. This principle has been successfully used in Section 30. A systematic mathematical method for exploiting symmetry properties requires, however, the use of the theory of group representation and is outside the scope of this book.

The equations of motion can be formulated in terms of the Cartesian components of the displacements. They are of the form (29.4). The vector $\mathbf{S}$ has $3N$ components. The $(3N)^2$ matrix elements of $\mathbf{A}$ must comply with conditions of the kind considered in (32.8). Usually the characteristic equation of the matrix has six solutions which are equal to zero. They express the fact that the interatomic forces cannot give rise to any resultant force or couple. In order to comply with this condition there are $18N$ equations between the matrix elements to be solved. This could in many instances be regarded as an unnecessary encumbrance. It can be avoided by the use of generalized coordinates the number of which can be smaller than the number of Cartesian displacements.

The position of the particles is then specified in terms of variables $(q_1, q_2 \ldots)$ which may be functions of any kind of the coordinates of the particles. There is no restriction concerning the admissible functions but in the equilibrium configuration all q_j are to be zero. The number of these 'generalized coordinates' q_j is usually smaller than the number of Cartesian components of the displacement, since they do not involve displacements or rotations of the whole molecule. In this way the mathematics is simplified at the cost of alternative complication.

The change in time of the generalized coordinates is determined by Lagrange's equations

$$\frac{\mathrm{d}}{\mathrm{d}t}\left(\frac{\partial L}{\partial \dot{q}_j}\right) - \frac{\partial L}{\partial q_j} = 0 \tag{33.1}$$

where $\dot{q}_j$ is the time derivative of q_j and L is the Lagrange function equal to the difference of kinetic and potential energy

$$L = E_{\mathrm{kin}} - E_{\mathrm{pot}} \tag{33.2}$$

in terms of the generalized coordinates and their time derivatives.

The potential energy is again, apart from a constant term, equal to a quadratic form $\tilde{\mathbf{q}}^*\mathbf{A}\mathbf{q}$ where $\mathbf{A}$ is a real symmetric matrix and $\mathbf{q}$ is a vector with the components q_j. The kinetic energy can also be written as a quadratic form $\tilde{\dot{\mathbf{q}}}^*\mathbf{G}\dot{\mathbf{q}}$. Here the matrix $\mathbf{G}$ is time independent and real symmetric. Its eigenvalues are positive (non-zero) but it is not necessarily a diagonal matrix.

In order to solve the equations of motion it is necessary to diagonalize $\mathbf{A}$ and $\mathbf{G}$ simultaneously by a congruent transformation. According to the theory of Section 24 this requires the solution of the determinantal equation

$$| \mathbf{A} - \gamma\mathbf{G} | = 0 \tag{33.3}$$

where γ is a parameter. The roots of this equation are equal to the ratio of the diagonal elements of the diagonalized matrices

$$\gamma_l = a'_{ll}/g'_{ll}$$

where $\mathbf{A}'$ and $\mathbf{G}'$ are diagonal matrices. It is assumed that these quantities are negative. If $\mathbf{T}$ is the transformation matrix so that $\mathbf{A}' = \tilde{\mathbf{T}}\mathbf{A}\mathbf{T}$ the displacement $\mathbf{q}$ is transformed according to $\mathbf{q} = \mathbf{U}\mathbf{q}'$ or $\tilde{\mathbf{q}} = \tilde{\mathbf{q}}'\mathbf{T}$. In terms of the transformed quantities the equations of motion are transformed to

$$\frac{\mathrm{d}}{\mathrm{d}t}\left(\frac{\partial L'}{\partial \dot{q}'_l}\right) - \frac{\partial L'}{\partial q'_l} = 0 \tag{33.4}$$

where L' is the Lagrange function in terms of the transformed quantities. If both matrices are diagonalized this is

$$g'_{ll}\frac{\mathrm{d}^2 q'_l}{\mathrm{d}t^2} + a'_{ll}q'_l = 0 \tag{33.5}$$

The solutions of this equation are simple harmonic oscillations with circular frequencies equal to $\omega_l^2 = -a'_{ll}/g'_{ll}$. Thus equation (33.3) leads directly to the frequencies.

In this method the force constants, or matrix elements of **A**, are not subject to any restrictive conditions except those which are due to the symmetry of the molecule. Nevertheless conditions similar to (32.7) have to be taken into account in a different context. The kinetic energy is, at first, given as a function of the Cartesian velocity components for which eventually the $\dot{q}_j$ are to be substituted. However, the latter are fewer than the former. Thus it is necessary to restrict the Cartesian velocity components by constraints; they are of such kind that the total linear momentum and the total angular momentum of the molecules are to vanish. Then it is possible to express the kinetic energy in terms of the $\dot{q}_j$ and the Lagrange function in terms of the q_j and $\dot{q}_j$.

Some insight into this method is provided by the example of the next section.

34. Triangular molecules

Consider again a triatomic molecule in which a central atom (2) of mass M is linked to atoms (1 and 3) each of mass m. These two are of the same kind and different from the central atom. Their equilibrium configuration is assumed to be an isosceles triangle.

Let the plane of the equilibrium configuration be the x–y plane. Then it is not necessary to consider movement in direction of the z axis since this will modify the movement in the x–y plane only by displacements and rotations of the whole molecule.

If the angle at the vertex 2 is denoted by β, generalized coordinates are defined as follows:

$$\begin{aligned} q_1 &= (x_3 - x_2)\cos\beta - (y_3 - y_2)\sin\beta \\ q_2 &= x_3 - x_1 \\ q_3 &= (x_2 - x_1)\cos\beta + (y_2 - y_1)\sin\beta \end{aligned} \tag{34.1}$$

These three degrees of freedom together with the three translational and three rotational degrees of freedom give a total of nine which is the correct number for a triatomic molecule. Equilibrium is to correspond to $q_1 = q_2 = q_3 = 0$. The changes of the angle β during oscillations are neglected.

The potential energy of the molecule is given as a function of the generalized coordinates by

$$E_{\text{pot}} = \tilde{\mathbf{q}}^* \mathbf{A}\mathbf{q}$$

involving at first six independent matrix elements. They are subject to symmetry conditions which are considered at a later stage.

The total linear momentum and the total angular momentum of the molecule should vanish; the angular momentum is taken about the mid-point of the line connecting atoms 1 and 3. The conditions are

$$\begin{aligned} m(\dot{x}_1 + \dot{x}_3) + M\dot{x}_2 &= 0 \\ m(\dot{y}_1 + \dot{y}_3) + M\dot{y}_2 &= 0 \\ m(\dot{y}_3 - \dot{y}_1)\cos\beta - M\dot{x}_2 \sin\beta &= 0 \end{aligned} \tag{34.2}$$

The last equation could have been derived also by taking the angular momentum about the centre of mass.

Equations (34.1) are to be differentiated with respect to the time; then the q_j on the left-hand side are replaced by $\dot{q}_j$. The Cartesian components of displacement on the right-hand side are replaced by the corresponding components of velocity. The resulting equations, together with (34.2) determine the Cartesian components of velocity uniquely as linear functions of the $\dot{q}_j$. Although the generalized coordinates are defined in purely geometrical terms the relation between the Cartesian and the generalized time derivatives (velocities) involves the masses m and M.

The resulting expressions are used for determining the kinetic energy in terms of the $\dot{q}_j$ as $E_{\text{kin}} = \tilde{\dot{\mathbf{q}}}^* \mathbf{G} \dot{\mathbf{q}}$. Finally the two matrices **A** and **G** are simultaneously diagonalized by solving a cubic equation of the form (33.3). This systematic procedure is elementary but unnecessarily cumbersome. In particular, the determinantal equation could be solved by numerical methods only. An alternative approach is now considered.

Simplifications are possible by appealing to molecular symmetry. In equilibrium the molecule has a plane of symmetry through atom 2, perpendicular to its plane and bisecting the angle β. If the molecule is distorted the plane converts x_3 to $-x_1$ and x_1 to $-x_3$; also x_2 to $-x_2$; y_1 to y_3 whereas y_2 is not affected. During the period of a mode of vibration the symmetry may be maintained throughout; alternatively every instantaneous asymmetric configuration must be matched by its mirror image during the same period at another instant. Symmetry is maintained if $x_1 = -x_3$ and $x_2 = 0$; also if $x_1 = x_2 = 0$ and $y_1 = y_3$. Asymmetry in a half period is compensated in the other half period if $x_1 = x_3$.

It is, accordingly, possible to define generalized coordinates which have the same symmetry properties as the modes of vibration:

$$\begin{aligned} r_1 &= x_1 - x_3 \\ r_2 &= y_1 + y_3 + \lambda y_2 \\ r_3 &= x_1 + x_3 + \mu x_2 \end{aligned} \tag{34.3}$$

where λ and μ are numerical parameters.

By differentiating equations (34.3) and taking account of (34.2) the Cartesian velocity components are expressed in terms of the time derivatives of the generalized coordinates.

$$\begin{aligned} \dot{x}_1 &= \tfrac{1}{2}(\dot{r}_1 + \dot{r}_3) & \dot{y}_1 &= \tfrac{1}{2}(\dot{r}_2 - \dot{r}_3) \\ \dot{x}_2 &= -(m/M)\dot{r}_3 & \dot{y}_2 &= (m/M)\dot{r}_2 \\ \dot{x}_3 &= \tfrac{1}{2}(-\dot{r}_1 + \dot{r}_3) & \dot{y}_3 &= \tfrac{1}{2}(\dot{r}_2 + \dot{r}_3 \tan \beta)^2 \end{aligned} \tag{34.4}$$

The kinetic energy is accordingly

$$\begin{aligned} E_{\text{kin}} &= \frac{m}{8}[(\dot{r}_1 + \dot{r}_3)^2 + (-\dot{r}_1 + \dot{r}_3)^2 + (\dot{r}_2 - \dot{r}_3 \tan \beta)^2 \\ &\qquad + (\dot{r}_2 + \dot{r}_3 \tan \beta)^2 + 4\dot{r}_2^2 + 4\dot{r}_3^2] \\ &= \tfrac{1}{4}m[\dot{r}_1^2 + 3\dot{r}_2^2 + \dot{r}_3^2(3 + \tan^2 \beta)] \end{aligned}$$

obtained as a sum of squares without any cross products so that the matrix $\mathbf{G}$ is diagonal.

The potential energy must be the same for the molecule and its mirror image. Therefore it must not change if simultaneously x_1 and x_3 are replaced by $-x_3$ and $-x_1$ respectively or if $-x_2$ is substituted for x_2. By expressing the $a_{jk}r_jr_k$ in terms of Cartesian displacements it is found that the factors of a_{13} and a_{23} do not satisfy these requirements so that a_{13} and a_{23} and the parameter μ must vanish.

The determinantal equation has accordingly the form

$$\begin{vmatrix} a_{11} - (m/4)\gamma & a_{12} & 0 \\ a_{12} & a_{22} - (3m/4)\gamma & 0 \\ 0 & 0 & a_{33} - \gamma(m/4)(3 + \tan^2 \beta) \end{vmatrix} = 0$$

The cubic equation is thus reduced to a linear and a quadratic equation. The solutions are

$$\gamma_1 = (4/m)a_{33}(3 + \tan^2 \beta)^{-1}$$

$$\left.\begin{matrix} \gamma_2 = \\ \gamma_3 = \end{matrix}\right\} \frac{4}{3m}\{\tfrac{1}{2}(3a_{11} + a_{22}) \pm [\tfrac{1}{4}(3a_{11} - a_{22})^2 + 3a_{12}^2]^{1/2}\}$$

If a_{11}, a_{22} and a_{33} are negative, γ_1, γ_2 and γ_3 determine the frequencies of the oscillations.

There are numerous molecules of this kind, water being the most important. However, as there are only three frequencies and four constants to be fitted a conclusive quantitative test of the theory has not yet been carried out. Otherwise the experimental data fit well to the theoretical results.

Spectra of molecules with a greater number of atoms can be analysed if they have a sufficiently high degree of symmetry.

CHAPTER 9

INVARIANCE, VECTORS AND TENSORS IN NATURAL SPACE

35. Space vectors

It is assumed that readers are familiar with the elementary vector methods which are usually included in courses of physics. In the present chapter it is intended to establish connections between the elementary properties of vectors with principles of invariance. Repetition of some elementary matters cannot be avoided but the present chapter is intended to be a supplement to the elementary approach rather than a substitute.

The extensive use of vector methods in physics is of recent origin. Vector notation in Maxwell's treatise on electromagnetic theory was regarded as an innovation comparable with the theory itself. It was not readily followed up. Vector methods were suspected of being incorrect; at the best they were regarded as a kind of shorthand that could be dispensed with. By now the critical objections have been disproved, but many physicists still regard brevity as the only merit of vector methods.

If an equation of physics claims general validity and is formulated in terms of some specific set of coordinates, its formulation in terms of alternative coordinates is not known automatically but requires explanation. However, if the equation is presented in terms of vector symbols no further explanation is required. Vector symbols are not tied to any particular set of coordinates but have an unambiguous meaning whatever coordinates are employed.

Consider first Cartesian coordinates with the origin fixed. Alternative sets are derived from each other by rotation, i.e. by changing the direction of the axes while preserving their orthogonality. It is known that equations expressing fundamental laws of physics have the same form before and after the rotation. In technical terms, the laws of physics are invariant with respect to rotations of the Cartesian axes, or briefly, natural space is isotropic. Vector symbols and the rules for handling them must be introduced in such a way that this isotropy is taken into account.

Space vectors are closely related to abstract vectors in three dimensions but definitions and notations are slightly modified. In accordance with Section 1 vectors are defined in terms of three numerical quantities (components). This is not stringent enough since space vectors must be endowed with the properties of magnitude and direction. Direction could be readily defined with respect to some particular set of coordinates but this is to be avoided. Therefore an indirect definition is required. Direction and magnitude are defined by stating in which way the components have to change when the axes are rotated.

The Cartesian coordinates of a point (x_1', x_2' and x_3') can be regarded as the components of a 'position vector' denoted by $\mathbf{r}'$. Rotation of the axes is expressed by an orthogonal transformation of the position vector

$$\mathbf{r}' = \mathbf{U}\mathbf{r}'' \tag{35.1}$$

where $\mathbf{U}$ is a real orthogonal matrix which determines the new coordinates or components of the transformed position vector $\mathbf{r}''$.

Space vectors are now introduced by the following definition.

DEFINITION (35.A) Space vectors are defined as a set of three Cartesian components (a_1', a_2' and a_3') which are real numbers and subject to the condition that a rotation of the coordinates of the form (35.1) determines new components according to

$$\mathbf{a}' = \mathbf{U}\mathbf{a}'' \tag{35.2}$$

where the matrix $\mathbf{U}$ is the same in (35.1) and (35.2).

According to this definition space vectors can be added and multiplied by scalars in accordance with the rules of Section 1. Equality of two vectors which is formulated in terms of some particular set of coordinates persists after transformation, since the same transformation rule is applied to both vectors. Thus in formulating any law of physics it is no longer necessary to distinguish between $\mathbf{a}'$, $\mathbf{a}''$ or any other vector derived from $\mathbf{a}'$ by orthogonal transformations. Instead a vector symbol $\mathbf{a}$ is used which is not tied to any specified set of components. Therefore every equation which is formulated in terms of vector symbols is automatically invariant with respect to rotations of the axes. This is the reason why equations of physics are preferably formulated in terms of vectors.

Displacement of the origin of the coordinates has the effect of adding the displacement $\mathbf{r}_0$ to every position vector whereas the components of non-localized vectors are not affected. The fundamental equations of physics are invariant with respect to these displacements.

The present approach to vectors is readily extended to entities of greater complexity, such as tensors and space–time vectors.

36. Products of vectors: Tensors

In elementary vector calculus the multiplication of vectors is introduced by defining the scalar product and the vector product of two vectors. There is an alternative multiplication of vectors which is now considered in some detail.

Let $\mathbf{a}'$ and $\tilde{\mathbf{b}}'$ be two space vectors.* The product $\mathbf{a}'\tilde{\mathbf{b}}'$ is defined in a way comparable to the direct product of matrices. The product $\mathbf{a}'\tilde{\mathbf{b}}'$ is called a dyadic and is expressed in the form of a three-by-three matrix the elements of which are the products of the vector components:

$$\mathbf{a}'\tilde{\mathbf{b}}' = \begin{bmatrix} a_1'\tilde{b}_1' & a_1'\tilde{b}_2' & a_2'\tilde{b}_3' \\ a_2'\tilde{b}_1' & a_2'\tilde{b}_2' & a_2'\tilde{b}_3' \\ a_3'\tilde{b}_1' & a_3'\tilde{b}_2' & a_3'\tilde{b}_3' \end{bmatrix} \tag{36.1}$$

The product of linear momentum and linear velocity of a molecule in the kinetic theory of gases is an example of a dyadic. The statistical expectation of the components of the dyadic are interpreted as the flow of momentum.

In accordance with the transformation rule (35.2)

$$\mathbf{a}' = \mathbf{U}\mathbf{a}'' \quad \tilde{\mathbf{b}}' = \tilde{\mathbf{b}}''\tilde{\mathbf{U}} = \tilde{\mathbf{b}}''\mathbf{U}^{-1}$$

the dyadic† is transformed as

$$\mathbf{a}'\tilde{\mathbf{b}}' = \mathbf{U}\mathbf{a}''\tilde{\mathbf{b}}''\mathbf{U}^{-1} \tag{36.2}$$

This is the familiar transformation rule for matrices. Once this transformation rule for dyadics has been established it is admissible to discard the reference to any set of coordinates and define dyadics in terms of vector symbols denoting them by $\mathbf{a}\tilde{\mathbf{b}}$ or simply $\mathbf{ab}$.

The transposed dyadic is denoted by

$$\widetilde{(\mathbf{ab})} = \mathbf{b}\tilde{\mathbf{a}} \tag{36.3}$$

* There is no need here to distinguish between row and column vectors. However, it helps in clarifying some of the deductions.

† The notation **ab** has been used in the early chapters of this book for denoting scalar products of abstract vectors. In accordance with prevailing conventions an alternative notation is used for space vectors. Thus the scalar product will be denoted by $\mathbf{p} \cdot \mathbf{q}$ and dyadics by **pq**.

and usually differs from $(\tilde{\mathbf{ab}})$. It is convenient to split dyadics into a symmetric and a skew-symmetric term:

$$\mathbf{ab} = \tfrac{1}{2}[\mathbf{ab} + (\widetilde{\mathbf{ab}})] + \tfrac{1}{2}[\mathbf{ab} - (\widetilde{\mathbf{ab}})] \tag{36.4}$$

Denoting the second term by $\mathbf{G}$ it is readily seen that $\mathbf{G} = -\widetilde{\mathbf{G}}$ and that this relation is orthogonally invariant. The diagonal elements of $\mathbf{G}$ must accordingly be zero. In order to derive the transformation rules for the non-diagonal elements it is necessary to consider some matrix $\mathbf{G}'$ which is defined in terms of a set of coordinates. Then the transformed matrix elements are obtained as

$$\begin{aligned}
g''_{23} &= g'_{23}(u_{22}u_{33} - u_{32}u_{23}) + g'_{13}(u_{12}u_{33} - u_{32}u_{13}) + g'_{12}(u_{12}u_{23} - u_{22}u_{13})\\
g''_{13} &= g'_{23}(u_{21}u_{33} - u_{31}u_{23}) + g'_{13}(u_{11}u_{33} - u_{31}u_{13}) + g'_{12}(u_{11}u_{23} - u_{21}u_{13})\\
g''_{12} &= g'_{23}(u_{21}u_{32} - u_{31}u_{22}) + g'_{13}(u_{11}u_{32} - u_{31}u_{12}) + g'_{12}(u_{11}u_{22} - u_{21}u_{12})
\end{aligned}$$

The coefficients in this transformation are equal to the cofactors of det $\mathbf{U}$; as $\mathbf{U}$ is real-orthogonal the cofactors are, by (20.9), equal to the matrix elements to which they are adjugated. Taking account of the definitions in Section 20 it follows that

$$\begin{aligned}
g''_{23} &= g'_{23}u_{11} - g'_{13}u_{21} + g'_{12}u_{31}\\
g''_{13} &= -g'_{23}u_{12} + g'_{13}u_{22} - g'_{12}u_{32}\\
g''_{12} &= g'_{23}u_{13} - g'_{13}u_{23} + g'_{12}u_{33}
\end{aligned} \tag{36.5}$$

It appears that the transformation of these matrix elements is the same as the transformation of a vector with the components

$$c'_1 = g'_{23} \quad c'_2 = -g'_{13} \quad c'_3 = g'_{12} \tag{36.6}$$

according to

$$\tilde{\mathbf{c}}'' = \tilde{\mathbf{c}}'\widetilde{\mathbf{U}}, \quad c'' = \mathbf{U}\mathbf{c}'$$

Thus under a transformation the skew-symmetric part of a dyadic can be replaced by a vector. Since vectors are defined in terms of their behaviour under transformations it may be said that the skew-symmetric part of a dyadic is a vector. The components of the vector $\mathbf{c}'$ are

$$\begin{aligned}
c'_1 &= \tfrac{1}{2}(a'_2b'_3 - a'_3b'_2)\\
c'_2 &= \tfrac{1}{2}(a'_3b'_1 - a'_1b'_3)\\
c'_3 &= \tfrac{1}{2}(a'_1b'_2 - a'_2b'_1)
\end{aligned}$$

Thus a vector symbol can be used for the skew-symmetric part of the dyadic; in accordance with current convention it is written as half the vector product of $\mathbf{a}$ and $\mathbf{b}$

$$\mathbf{c} = \tfrac{1}{2}(\mathbf{a} \times \mathbf{b}) \tag{36.7}$$

The symmetric part of a dyadic cannot be reduced to a vector. It has nine matrix elements of which six are independent. According to the transformation rule (36.2) and by (21.E) the property of being symmetric is preserved under orthogonal transformations. The trace of the symmetric part is equal to the trace of the dyadic itself and a scalar. It is equal to the scalar product $\mathbf{a} \cdot \mathbf{b}$ of the vectors **a** and **b**. Otherwise there is little to comment on the properties of the symmetric term.

Whereas the use of dyadics is limited there are important entities in physics which have nine components. Every component is associated with a pair of Cartesian coordinates. If the components are regarded as matrix elements they obey the transformation rule (36.2). They are called tensors of the second order or, if no ambiguity arises, simply tensors.

Skew-symmetric tensors can, like skew-symmetric dyadics, be considered as vectors (although not necessarily a vector product). Symmetric tensors have little in common with vectors since they are associated with two directions rather than a single one. As an example consider the stresses in an elastic body from which the term 'tensor' is derived. The stress is a force acting on an (possibly infinitesimal) area. It depends upon the direction of the force and upon the direction of the normal to the area.

The trace of a tensor is a scalar (although not necessarily a scalar product). The product of a tensor and a vector is denoted by a dot and results in a vector. Thus $\tilde{\mathbf{a}} \cdot \mathbf{B}$ and $\mathbf{C} \cdot \mathbf{f}$ are vectors. The product of two vectors and a tensor is written with two dots $\mathbf{a} \cdot \mathbf{B} \cdot \mathbf{c}$ and is a scalar. The product of two tensors according to the rule of matrix multiplication is written by a dot, $\mathbf{A} \cdot \mathbf{B}$ and results in a tensor. The trace of a product of two tensors is written with two dots $\mathbf{A} : \mathbf{B}$ and is a scalar.

Given a symmetric tensor $\mathbf{A}'$ it is always possible to find a set of Cartesian coordinates with respect to which the non-diagonal elements of $\mathbf{A}''$ vanish.

Vectors as defined in the preceding section and tensors as defined in this section are not localized. Localized vectors and tensors are connected with some particular value of the position vector. This may be a single point in space, a continuous distribution or anything between these extremes. Thus localized vectors and tensors are functions of the position vector although not necessarily analytic functions.

Whereas vectors are readily visualized as being of definite length and orientation there is no simple and general geometrical model that applies to tensors. However, if a tensor **B** is determined by the way of a linear relation between vectors **p** and **q**

$$\mathbf{q} = \mathbf{B} \cdot \mathbf{p} \tag{36.8}$$

a geometrical representation of the tensor can be given. Assuming that the eigenvalues of the tensor are positive let their reciprocals be the semi-axes of an ellipsoid. The centre of the ellipsoid is to coincide with the origin and the direction of the axes is to be the same as the direction of the eigenvectors. If a radius vector in the direction of **p** is plotted from the origin it marks a point on the surface of the ellipsoid. Consider the tangential plane through that point and the perpendicular distance of that plane from the origin. The direction of this perpendicular distance vector is equal to the direction of the vector **q**. It is not necessary to present the proof in this book because the geometrical construction is of little use and equations (36.8) are easy to solve.

An example of a symmetric tensor is provided by the moments of inertia of rigid bodies. Let **J** be a tensor with the Cartesian components

$$J_{jk} = (2\delta_{jk} - 1) \int \rho(r) r_j r_k \, d\mathbf{r} \qquad (36.9)$$

Here r_j and r_k are the Cartesian coordinates of any point in the interior of the body and **r** its position vector. ρ is the density and d**r** is the volume element. The integral is to be extended over the whole volume of the body; δ_{jk} are the components of the unit matrix. The eigenvectors of **J** are called *principal axes of inertia.*

J is localized at the centre of the body and is of importance in the dynamics of rigid bodies. If **L** is the angular momentum localized at the centre of mass and **ω** is the angular velocity, localized at any point inside the rigid body, these vectors are related by

$$\mathbf{L} = \mathbf{J} \cdot \boldsymbol{\omega} \qquad (36.10)$$

The rotational movement of the bodies is determined by (36.10) together with

$$d\mathbf{L}/dt = \mathbf{C} \qquad (36.11)$$

where **C** is the couple of external forces at the centre of mass.

Even a superficial knowledge of spinning tops shows that the solution of these equations is in general of a complex nature. A simple type of movement persists only in the absence of external couples and on condition that the initial angular velocity has the same direction as a principal axis of inertia. Then **L** and **ω** are parallel and the velocity stays constant, both in magnitude and direction.

37. Fields

Localized scalars, vectors or tensors which are continuously distributed in space are called fields. Scalar, vector and tensor fields may be mutually related by differentiation with respect to the coordinates.

If a scalar a is given as a function of the Cartesian coordinates (or of the position vector) it represents a scalar field and is mathematically specified as $a(r')$. The three partial differential coefficients $\partial a/\partial x_1'$, $\partial a/\partial x_2'$ and $\partial a/\partial x_3'$ are components of a vector, to be denoted by $\nabla' a$.

In proving this assertion the transformation rule is rewritten as

$$\mathbf{r}' = \mathbf{U}\mathbf{r}'' \qquad \mathbf{r}'' = \mathbf{U}^{-1}\mathbf{r}' \tag{37.1}$$

$$u_{jk} = \partial x_j'/\partial x_k'' \quad u_{kj}^{-1} = \partial x_k''/\partial x_j'$$

The partial differentiation in the first equation (37.1) is performed with two of the doubly primed coordinates being held constant; the partial differentiation in the second equation is performed with two of the singly primed coordinates being held constant.

Since $\mathbf{U}$ is an orthogonal matrix it follows that

$$\partial x_j'/\partial x_k'' = \partial x_k''/\partial x_j' \tag{37.2}$$

The differential coefficients of a with respect to the two sets of coordinates are related by

$$\frac{\partial a}{\partial x_j'} = \sum_k \left(\frac{\partial a}{\partial x_k''}\right)\left(\frac{\partial x_k''}{\partial x_j'}\right)$$

and, by (37.1) and (37.2) this is

$$\frac{\partial a}{\partial x_j'} = \sum_k \left(\frac{\partial a}{\partial x_k''}\right)\left(\frac{\partial x_j'}{\partial x_k''}\right) = \sum_k u_{jk}\frac{\partial a}{\partial x_k''}$$

It follows then that

$$\nabla' a = \mathbf{U}\nabla'' a \tag{37.3}$$

Thus it is shown that $\nabla' a$ obeys the transformation rule (35.2) and is, accordingly, a vector corresponding to the vector symbol ∇a. As the above deduction applies to the differential operator ∇ as well as to the differential coefficients, the operator ∇ itself is a vector symbol. Alternative notations for this operator are **grad** and $\partial/\partial\mathbf{r}$. It is seen that this operator can be employed for deriving a vector field from a scalar field.

Once it is understood that ∇ is a vector it follows, virtually without any proof, that the corresponding differentiations of vector fields can be considered as products of the vector into some other vector. In particular if $\mathbf{b}(\mathbf{r})$ represents a vector field then $\nabla\mathbf{b}$ (or $\partial\mathbf{b}/\partial\mathbf{r}$) represents a tensor field. If the transpose is denoted by $(\widetilde{\nabla\mathbf{b}})$ the tensor is resolved into skew-symmetric and symmetric components.

$$\nabla\mathbf{b} = \tfrac{1}{2}[\nabla\mathbf{b} - (\widetilde{\nabla\mathbf{b}})] + \tfrac{1}{2}[\nabla\mathbf{b} + (\widetilde{\nabla\mathbf{b}})] \tag{37.4}$$

The first term represents, in accordance with (36.7), a vector field. Its components are

$$\frac{1}{2}\left(\frac{\partial b_3}{\partial x_2} - \frac{\partial b_2}{\partial x_3}\right); \quad \frac{1}{2}\left(\frac{\partial b_1}{\partial x_3} - \frac{\partial b_3}{\partial x_1}\right); \quad \frac{1}{2}\left(\frac{\partial b_2}{\partial x_1} - \frac{\partial b_1}{\partial x_2}\right)$$

In conventional notation they are the components of $\frac{1}{2}$ (**curl b**). The second term in (37.4) is a symmetric tensor; its trace is a scalar. This trace is called the divergence of **b** and is written as

$$\operatorname{div} \mathbf{b}, \quad \nabla \cdot \mathbf{b} \quad \text{or} \quad (\partial/\partial \mathbf{r}) \cdot \mathbf{b}$$

Of the second order differential operators the most important is Laplace's operator. It is defined as $\nabla \cdot \nabla$ or $(\partial/\partial \mathbf{r}) \cdot (\partial/\partial \mathbf{r})$ and usually denoted by ∇^2. It is a scalar and, hence

$$\nabla^2 a = \partial^2 a/\partial x_1^2 + \partial^2 a/\partial x_2^2 + \partial^2 a/\partial x_3^2$$

is also a scalar. If C represents a tensor field the expression $\nabla \cdot \mathsf{C}$ (where ∇ is considered to be a row vector) represents a vector field which may be called the divergence of the tensor.

An important example is the vector field

$$\nabla \cdot \nabla \mathbf{b}$$

which has the components

$$\sum_j \partial^2 b_k/\partial x_j^2$$

As they are similar to the Laplace operator some authors use the notation $\nabla^2 \mathbf{b}$. This similarity is, however, restricted to Cartesian components.—By performing the differentiations in coordinates the identity is established

$$\nabla \cdot \nabla \mathbf{b} = \nabla(\nabla \cdot \mathbf{b}) - \nabla \times (\nabla \times \mathbf{b}) = \mathbf{grad} \operatorname{div} \mathbf{b} - \mathbf{curl}\, \mathbf{curl}\, \mathbf{b}$$

38. Strain and stress

Important examples of tensor fields are provided by the mechanics of continuous matter. Consider in particular an elastic body and let the origin of coordinates be placed at the centre of mass. Let the particles of which the body consists be moved over small distances and assume that the local displacement ($\mathbf{u}$) can be expressed as a function of the position vector ($\mathbf{r}$):

$$\mathbf{u} = \mathbf{u}(\mathbf{r})$$
$$\mathbf{u}(O) = O$$

This represents a vector field. It can be expanded as

$$\mathbf{u} = (\partial \mathbf{u}/\partial \mathbf{r}) \cdot \mathbf{r} + O(r^2) \tag{38.1}$$

The tensor $\partial \mathbf{u}/\partial \mathbf{r}$ is split into a skew-symmetric and a symmetric part; the former is equal to $\frac{1}{2}$ **curl u**. If it were uniform it would describe a rotation of the body about the centre of mass. In general both the symmetric and the skew-symmetric parts are functions of the position. The symmetric part of the tensor

$$\boldsymbol{\epsilon} = \frac{1}{2}\left(\frac{\partial \mathbf{u}}{\partial \mathbf{r}} + \widetilde{\frac{\partial \mathbf{u}}{\partial \mathbf{r}}}\right) \tag{38.2}$$

has the components

$$\varepsilon_{jj} = \frac{\partial u_j}{\partial x_j} \quad \varepsilon_{jk} = \varepsilon_{kj} = \frac{1}{2}\left(\frac{\partial u_j}{\partial x_k} + \frac{\partial u_k}{\partial x_j}\right)$$

and is called the strain tensor. Its trace

$$\varepsilon_{11} + \varepsilon_{22} + \varepsilon_{33} = \nabla \cdot \mathbf{u}$$

is equal to the local increment in specific volume divided by the initial specific volume. The tensor

$$\boldsymbol{\gamma} = \boldsymbol{\epsilon} - \tfrac{1}{3}(\text{tr}\ \boldsymbol{\epsilon})\mathbf{I} \tag{38.3}$$

is a measure for the local change in shape after the change in volume has been taken into account. The strain tensor is dimensionless and, as all displacements are assumed to be small, the strain components are small compared with unity.

Thus the vector field of displacements can be expressed in terms of the vector field of local rotation and the tensor field of strain.

The forces in an elastic body are expressed in terms of another tensor, that is the stress tensor $\boldsymbol{\sigma}$. It determines forces per unit of area, acting on any infinitesimal area in the interior or on the surface of the elastic body. The specific properties are due to the fact that the force and its reaction attack at the same point. Thus the direction in which the force acts is reversed by 180° if the area is approached from the opposite direction. Every component of stress is associated with two directions in space, the direction of the normal on the infinitesimal area and the direction of the force acting on it. The component σ_{12} for example is equal to the component of force in the x_2 direction acting on an infinitesimal area with a normal in the positive x_1 direction. The trace of the stress tensor is equal to (—3) times the isotropic pressure (also called hydrostatic pressure). The tensor

$$\boldsymbol{\tau} = \boldsymbol{\sigma} - \tfrac{1}{3}(\text{tr}\ \boldsymbol{\sigma})\mathbf{I} \tag{38.4}$$

determines the excess of the stress components over the local negative pressure. These components depend on the direction but are not vectors.

In the theory of elasticity, in particular that of elastic equilibrium, one has to determine the distribution of stresses if the local displacements are given or *vice versa*. In either case it is necessary to start with some general relation between the forces and the displacements. A relation of this kind is known as Hooke's law, according to which local stresses are independent of the local curl of the displacement and linear functions of the local strain. If the assumption is added that the material of which the body consists is isotropic the form of the strain–stress relation is completely determined.

As the traces of the strain and the stress tensors are scalars their mutual dependence must be independent of the other components.

Hence the decrease in the isotropic pressure must be proportional to the relative increment in specific volume.

The tensors $\boldsymbol{\gamma}$ and $\boldsymbol{\tau}$ must also be proportional to each other:

$$(1/3)\,\mathrm{tr}\,\boldsymbol{\sigma} = \mathrm{K}\,\mathrm{tr}\,\boldsymbol{\epsilon}$$
$$[\boldsymbol{\sigma} - (1/3)(\mathrm{tr}\,\boldsymbol{\sigma})\mathbf{I}] = 2\mathrm{s}[\boldsymbol{\epsilon} - (1/3)(\mathrm{tr}\,\boldsymbol{\epsilon})\mathbf{I}] \tag{38.5}$$

The constants K and S are independent of each other and have to be taken from experiment. They are known as bulk modulus and shear modulus respectively. In anisotropic materials the equations (38.5) would have a more complex form and involve a larger number of constants.

Although equations (38.5) are correct they are unsuitable for application since they involve seven scalar equations whereas there are only six unknown quantities which may be components of the strain or the stress tensor. The number of equations is, however, readily reduced. If the first equation is multiplied by $\mathbf{I}$ and added to the second equation we obtain

$$\boldsymbol{\sigma} = 2\mathrm{s}\boldsymbol{\epsilon} + (\mathrm{K} - \tfrac{2}{3}\mathrm{s})(\mathrm{tr}\,\boldsymbol{\epsilon})\mathbf{I} \tag{38.6}$$

as a complete expression for Hooke's law.

It may be desirable to employ alternative elastic constants which are closer related to measurements. For this purpose consider the dilatation of a fibre of circular or square cross section. Let the x_3 axis coincide with the axis of the fibre; let the fibre be stretched without any forces acting on the lateral surfaces. Then $\sigma'_{11} = \sigma'_{22} = 0$; also all non-diagonal components of the strain and stress tensor are zero and $\varepsilon'_{11} = \varepsilon'_{22}$ by reason of symmetry.

Then equations (38.6) reduce to

$$(2\mathrm{K} + \tfrac{2}{3}\mathrm{s})\varepsilon'_{11} + (\mathrm{K} - \tfrac{2}{3}\mathrm{s})\varepsilon'_{33} = 0$$
$$(2\mathrm{K} - \tfrac{2}{3}\mathrm{s})\varepsilon'_{11} + (\mathrm{K} + \tfrac{4}{3}\mathrm{s})\varepsilon'_{33} = \sigma_{33} \tag{38.7}$$

By eliminating ε_{11} it follows that

$$\sigma_{33} = \frac{9\mathrm{KS}}{3\mathrm{K} + \mathrm{S}}\varepsilon_{33} \tag{38.8}$$

and from the first equation (38.1) it follows that

$$\varepsilon_{11} = -\left[\frac{3(\mathrm{K} - 2\mathrm{S})}{2(3\mathrm{K} + \mathrm{S})}\right]\varepsilon_{33} \tag{38.9}$$

Denoting the bracket expressions in (38.8) and (38.9) by E (Young's modulus) and ν (Poisson's ratio) respectively and expressing K and S in terms of these two new constants, Hooke's law can be rewritten in the form

$$\boldsymbol{\sigma} = \frac{\mathrm{E}}{1 + \nu}\left[\boldsymbol{\epsilon} + \frac{\nu}{1 - 2\nu}(\mathrm{tr}\,\varepsilon)\mathbf{I}\right] \tag{38.10}$$

Elastic equilibrium is determined by the relation

$$\nabla \cdot \boldsymbol{\sigma} + \mathbf{F} = 0 \tag{38.11}$$

where **F** is the force per unit volume ('body force') acting on the elastic body. The most important body force is gravity. Substitution of (38.2) into (38.10) and (38.11) results in

$$\frac{E}{1+\nu}\left[\nabla \cdot \nabla \mathbf{u} + \frac{1}{1-2\nu}\nabla\nabla \cdot \mathbf{u}\right] + \mathbf{F} = 0 \tag{38.12}$$

This set of simultaneous equations determines the field of displacements if the field of forces and appropriate boundary conditions are given. By substituting the product of density and acceleration, i.e. $\rho\partial^2\mathbf{u}/\partial t^2$ on the right-hand side of (38.12) equations are obtained which determine the propagation of elastic waves.

39. Spherical polar coordinates

Problems in field theories frequently require the use of curvilinear, in particular spherical polar, coordinates. The fundamental equations of physics are not affected by rotations of the Cartesian axes but they change their form if rectilinear coordinates are replaced by curvilinear ones. Nevertheless the formalism of vector calculus applies whatever coordinates are used provided that the vector symbols admit an unambiguous interpretation. As far as spherical polar coordinates are concerned the interpretation of vector symbols is based on the fact that within small volumes the local set of polar coordinates differs from the Cartesian set merely by the orientation of the axes.

Spherical polar coordinates are denoted by r, ϑ and ϕ and are defined by a non-linear transformation

$$\begin{aligned} x_1 &= r \sin\vartheta \cos\phi \\ x_2 &= r \sin\vartheta \sin\phi \\ x_3 &= r \cos\vartheta \end{aligned} \tag{39.1}$$

Surfaces of constant r are spherical; ϑ (varying from 0 to π) determines the latitude and ϕ (varying from 0 to 2π) determines the longitude on spherical surfaces. r can vary from 0 to ∞. The volume element is

$$\mathrm{d}x_1\mathrm{d}x_2\mathrm{d}x_3 = r^2 \sin\vartheta \,\mathrm{d}r\,\mathrm{d}\vartheta\,\mathrm{d}\phi$$

Let position vectors in this section be denoted by **s**. 'Components' of this vector would not have any simple meaning. However, the infinitesimal increments ds still obey the transformation rule (35.2). By differentiating (39.1) it appears that

$$\mathrm{d}\mathbf{s}' = \mathbf{U}\,\mathrm{d}\mathbf{s}'' \tag{39.2}$$

where here and subsequently the single prime refers to Cartesian coordinates and the double prime to the curvilinear set. The transformation matrix is orthogonal.

$$\mathbf{U} = \begin{bmatrix} \sin\vartheta\cos\phi & \cos\vartheta\cos\phi & -\sin\vartheta\sin\phi \\ \sin\vartheta\sin\phi & \cos\vartheta\sin\phi & \sin\vartheta\cos\phi \\ \cos\vartheta & -\sin\vartheta & 0 \end{bmatrix} \tag{39.3}$$

Hence

$$ds'^2 = ds''^2 = ds_1''^2 + ds_2''^2 + ds_3''^3$$

where

$$ds_1'' = dr; \quad ds_2'' = r\, d\vartheta; \quad ds_3'' = r \sin\vartheta\, d\phi \tag{39.4}$$

Curvilinear components of vectors (other than position vectors) are derived from their Cartesian components by the transformation inverse to (39.2). The same transformation matrix is used for transforming Cartesian tensor components in accordance with the rule (36.2). The r, ϑ and ϕ components of vectors will be denoted by 1, 2 and 3 respectively.

Once this connection between the Cartesian and curvilinear components of vectors and tensors is established the interpretation of vector symbols follows almost automatically. Multiplication rules for forming the dyadic, vector and scalar products are the same as before, if Cartesian are replaced by curvilinear components.

The vector field ∇a can be interpreted by transforming its Cartesian components. Its direct definition implies that the limit $\Delta\mathbf{s} = 0$ is taken of $\Delta a/\Delta\mathbf{s}$. Thus

$$\nabla_1'' = \frac{\partial}{\partial r}; \quad \nabla_2'' = \frac{1}{r}\frac{\partial}{\partial\vartheta}; \quad \nabla_3'' = \frac{1}{r\sin\vartheta}\frac{\partial}{\partial\phi} \tag{39.5}$$

Differentiation of vector fields requires some care. Spatial derivatives must take account not only of changes in magnitude and direction but also of location. Even if the vector field were uniform the curvilinear components would vary from point to point on account of the changing directions of the meridians and parallels. Therefore the components of $(\nabla\tilde{\mathbf{b}})''$ are not equal to the result of operating with ∇'' on the vector $\tilde{\mathbf{b}}''$.

It is necessary to express at first the Cartesian vectors ∇' and $\tilde{\mathbf{b}}'$ in terms of their curvilinear components:

$$\nabla' = \mathbf{U}\nabla'' \quad \tilde{\mathbf{b}}' = \tilde{\mathbf{b}}''\mathbf{U}^{-1}$$

From these expressions the Cartesian tensor

$$\nabla'\tilde{\mathbf{b}}' = \mathbf{U}(\nabla''\tilde{\mathbf{b}}''\mathbf{U}^{-1})$$

is obtained. Here the bracket indicates that ∇'' operates on the product of the two and only two following quantities. Having obtained the Cartesian expression it is now transformed back to polar coordinates.

Hence

$$(\nabla\tilde{\mathbf{b}})'' = \mathbf{U}^{-1}\mathbf{U}(\nabla''\tilde{\mathbf{b}}''\mathbf{U}^{-1})\mathbf{U} = (\nabla''\tilde{\mathbf{b}}''\mathbf{U}^{-1})\mathbf{U} \tag{39.6}$$

By this method of transforming the Cartesian components all symbols of vector algebra and calculus can be interpreted in terms of spherical polar coordinates. It is not necessary to follow this up. In conclusion the most important formulae are compiled.

$$\nabla\tilde{\mathbf{b}}'' = \begin{bmatrix} \dfrac{\partial b_1''}{\partial r} & \dfrac{\partial b_2''}{\partial r} & \dfrac{\partial b_3''}{\partial r} \\ \dfrac{1}{r}\left(\dfrac{\partial b_1''}{\partial \vartheta} - b_2''\right) & \dfrac{1}{r}\left(\dfrac{\partial b_2''}{\partial \vartheta} + b_1''\right) & \dfrac{1}{r}\dfrac{\partial b_3''}{\partial \vartheta} \\ \dfrac{1}{r}\left(\dfrac{\partial b_1''}{\sin\vartheta\,\partial\phi} - b_3''\right) & \dfrac{1}{r\sin\vartheta}\left(\dfrac{\partial b_2''}{\partial\phi} - b_3''\cos\vartheta\right) & \dfrac{1}{r}\left(\dfrac{\partial b_3''}{\sin\vartheta\,\partial\phi} + \dfrac{b_2''}{\tan\vartheta} + b_1''\right) \end{bmatrix} \tag{39.7}$$

$$\operatorname{div}\tilde{\mathbf{b}}'' = \frac{\partial b_1''}{\partial r} + \frac{2b_1''}{r} + \frac{\partial b_2''}{r\,\partial\vartheta} + \frac{b_2''}{r\tan\vartheta} + \frac{\partial b_3''}{r\sin\vartheta\,\partial\phi} \tag{39.8}$$

$$\left.\begin{aligned} \operatorname{curl}_1\mathbf{b}'' &= \frac{1}{r\sin\vartheta}\left[\frac{\partial b_2''}{\partial\phi} - \frac{\partial}{\partial\vartheta}(b_3''\sin\vartheta)\right] \\ \operatorname{curl}_2\mathbf{b}'' &= \frac{1}{r}\left[\frac{\partial}{\partial r}(rb_3'') - \frac{1}{\sin\vartheta}\frac{\partial b_1''}{\partial\phi}\right] \\ \operatorname{curl}_3\mathbf{b}'' &= \frac{1}{r}\left[\frac{\partial b_1''}{\partial\vartheta} - \frac{\partial(rb_2'')}{\partial r}\right] \end{aligned}\right\} \tag{39.9}$$

$$\nabla^2 a = \frac{1}{r^2}\frac{\partial}{\partial r}r^2\frac{\partial a}{\partial r} + \frac{1}{r^2\sin\vartheta}\frac{\partial}{\partial\vartheta}\sin\vartheta\frac{\partial a}{\partial\vartheta} + \frac{1}{r^2\sin^2\vartheta}\frac{\partial^2 a}{\partial\phi^2} \tag{39.10}$$

There are other types of orthogonal curvilinear coordinates than the spherical which can be derived from the Cartesian by an orthogonal transformation. The most important of these are the cylindrical, paraboloidal and ellipsoidal coordinates. The interpretation of vector symbols in terms of these coordinates proceeds in close analogy to the arguments of the present section.

40. Space–time vectors

If the isotropy of natural space should become the object of critical scrutiny it would be argued that the phenomena of physics are compatible with the use of vector and tensor methods. In particular all observable quantities are scalars, vectors or tensors. This is sufficient for establishing isotropy and could be refuted only by exhibiting phenomena which could not be specified in those terms.

In particular in the theory of relativity a generalization of vector and tensor methods has indeed played an important part. The theory of relativity claims *ex hypothesi* that the equations of physics are to be invariant with respect to certain transformations which are to some extent similar to the rotations of Cartesian axes. On account of this similarity additional types of vectors and tensors have been introduced to physics. If the equations of physics are formulated in terms of the generalized vector symbols their postulated invariance is automatically established. In the present section this branch of vector methods is surveyed to that extent as it is used in special relativity. It is assumed that readers are familiar with the essential features of the theory.

The equations of Newtonian mechanics are invariant with respect to transformations of the Cartesian coordinates which include not only the rotation of the axes but also time-dependent displacements of the origin:

$$\mathbf{r}'' = \mathbf{U}\mathbf{r}' - \mathbf{v}t \tag{40.1}$$

Here $\mathbf{U}$ can be any real orthogonal matrix and $\mathbf{v}$ is a constant velocity determining the relative movement of the two origins; t is the time. This relation between two frames of reference is called a Galileo transformation. If the axes in the two sets have the same directions the transformation simplifies to

$$x_1'' = x_1' - v_1 t; \quad x_2'' = x_2'; \quad x_3'' = x_3'; \quad v_2 = v_3 = 0 \tag{40.2}$$

The corresponding rule for transforming velocities ($\mathbf{u}$) is

$$u_1'' = u_1' - v; \quad u_2'' = u_2'; \quad u_3'' = u_3' \tag{40.3}$$

In the special theory of relativity a different transformation rule applies. In contrast to (40.1) it involves not only the position vector but also the time. In formulating the transformation rule it is convenient to introduce vectors of four dimensions. The particular form of these vectors is then chosen in such a way that the resulting formulae reduce to those of ordinary Newtonian mechanics in the limit $v \ll c$ (c being the speed of light *in vacuo*). Thus a 'four-vector $\mathbf{x}'$' is defined in such a way that the components x_1', x_2', x_3' are Cartesian coordinates and $x_4' = ict'$, where t' is the time measured with respect to a particular frame of reference. The transformation rule is then the 'Lorentz transformation'

$$\mathbf{x}'' = \mathbf{V}\mathbf{x}' \tag{40.4}$$

where
$$\mathbf{V} = \mathbf{W} + \mathbf{P} + \mathbf{Q} \tag{40.5}$$

with

$$\mathbf{W} = \begin{bmatrix} & \mathbf{U} & & 0 \\ & & & 0 \\ & & & 0 \\ 0 & 0 & 0 & 0 \end{bmatrix}$$

the three-by-three sub-matrix $\mathbf{U}$ being real orthogonal.

$$\mathbf{P} = \left\{-1 + \left[1 - \left(\frac{v}{c}\right)^2\right]^{-1/2}\right\} v^{-2} \begin{bmatrix} v_1^2 & v_1 v_2 & v_1 v_3 & 0 \\ v_1 v_2 & v_2^2 & v_2 v_3 & 0 \\ v_1 v_3 & v_2 v_3 & v_3^2 & 0 \\ 0 & 0 & 0 & 0 \end{bmatrix}$$

$$\mathbf{Q} = \frac{i}{c}\left[1 - \left(\frac{v}{c}\right)^2\right]^{-1/2} \begin{bmatrix} 0 & 0 & 0 & v_1 \\ 0 & 0 & 0 & v_2 \\ 0 & 0 & 0 & v_3 \\ -v_1 & -v_2 & -v_3 & -ic \end{bmatrix}$$

The matrix $\mathbf{V}$ is complex-orthogonal. For most purposes it is not necessary to consider the transformation in its most general form. It is sufficient to put $\mathbf{U} = \mathbf{I}$ and $v_2 = v_3 = 0$, $v_1 = v$. Then the special transformation, corresponding to (40.2), is determined by the matrix

$$\mathbf{V} = \left[1 - \left(\frac{v}{c}\right)^2\right]^{-1/2} \begin{bmatrix} 1 & 0 & 0 & i(v/c) \\ 0 & [1 - (v/c)^2]^{1/2} & 0 & 0 \\ 0 & 0 & [1 - (v/c)^2]^{1/2} & 0 \\ -i(v/c) & 0 & 0 & 1 \end{bmatrix} \tag{40.6}$$

The corresponding transformation of velocities differs from the non-relativistic relation (40.3) and is given by

$$\begin{aligned} u_1'' &= \frac{u_1' - v}{1 - (u_1 v/c^2)} \\ u_2'' &= \frac{u_2'[1 - (v/c)^2]^{1/2}}{1 - (u_1 v/c^2)} \\ u_3'' &= \frac{u_3'[1 - (v/c)^2]^{1/2}}{1 - (u_1 v/c^2)} \end{aligned} \tag{40.7}$$

In contrast to (40.3) the velocity components perpendicular to the relative velocity of the two frames of reference are affected by the transformation.

The magnitude of the position vector is invariant:

$$x'^2 = -c^2 t'^2 + x_1'^2 + x_2'^2 + x_3'^2; \quad x'^2 = x''^2$$

Four-vectors are now defined as four-component abstract vectors which comply with the transformation rule (40.4), such as laid down for 'position vectors' **x**. According to the special theory of relativity all equations should be invariant with respect to Lorentz transformations. This can be demonstrated by formulating them in terms of four-vector symbols, or in terms of tensors derived from these vectors by the methods of Section 36. Whereas vector formalism was a matter of convenience as far as natural space is concerned, it is here an important method for testing the consistency of the space–time theories.

The electromagnetic theory according to Maxwell and Lorentz has the property of being invariant with respect to Lorentz transformations. It is merely necessary to apply a suitable notation for demonstrating this invariance by the use of vector notation. Thus a four-vector $\mathbf{A}'$ is defined; the first three components are supposed to be equal to the components of the vector potential; the fourth component is equal to the scalar potential. Another four-vector $\mathbf{J}'$ has three components equal to the components of current density, the fourth component being equal to the density of charge multiplied by c. Denoting the d'Alembert operator

$$\frac{\partial^2}{\partial x_1^2}+\frac{\partial^2}{\partial x_2^2}+\frac{\partial^2}{\partial x_3^2}-\frac{\partial^2}{c^2\partial t^2}$$

by $\Box$ the equation determining the propagation of electromagnetic waves becomes

$$(4\pi J_n/c)-\Box A_n=0 \quad (n=1\ldots 4)$$

where the first term vanishes in the absence of matter. Similarly other relations of electromagnetic theory admit formulation in terms of four-vectors.

Newtonian mechanics is not compatible with the claims of Lorentz invariance. The essential innovations due to special relativity were accordingly the changes applied to the equations of mechanics. In the mechanical equations of motion the time plays the part of an independent variable whereas the positions of particles are dependent variables. This approach is incompatible with Lorentz invariance. Thus another independent variable is employed. The differential $\mathrm{d}s$, defined by

$$\mathrm{d}s^2=\frac{-\mathrm{d}x^2}{c^2}=\mathrm{d}t^2-\left(\frac{\mathrm{d}x_1^2+\mathrm{d}x_2^2+\mathrm{d}x_3^2}{c^2}\right)$$

is called the differential of invariant time and is a scalar. It is employed as the independent variable in particle mechanics. The substitution of $\mathrm{d}s$ for $\mathrm{d}t$ as the independent variable is virtually sufficient for introducing the necessary changes in the laws of mechanics. If the Newtonian velocity is defined as

$$u'_1 = \frac{dx'_1}{dt}; \quad u'_2 = \frac{dx'_2}{dt}; \quad u'_3 = \frac{dx'_3}{dt}$$

$$u'^2 = u'^2_1 + u'^2_2 + u'^2_3$$

it is readily ascertained that

$$\frac{dt}{ds} = \left(\frac{ds}{dt}\right)^{-1} = \left[1 - \left(\frac{u'}{c}\right)^2\right]^{-1/2}$$

A velocity four-vector is now defined as

$$\mathbf{q} = \frac{d\mathbf{x}}{ds}$$

Its components are

$$q'_j = u'_j\left[1 - \left(\frac{u'}{c}\right)^2\right]^{-1/2} \quad (j = 1, 2, 3)$$

$$q'_4 = \frac{dx'_4}{ds} = ic\left[1 - \left(\frac{u'}{c}\right)^2\right]^{-1/2} \tag{40.8}$$

For a mass point of mass m the product $m\mathbf{q}$ plays the part of momentum and the equations of motion are:

$$\frac{d}{ds}(m\mathbf{q}') = \mathbf{F}' \tag{40.9}$$

The four-vector on the right-hand side has three components representing the force in accordance with its meaning in experiments. The fourth component has actually to be defined in such a way that equation (40.9) is satisfied. The mass m is a scalar and a constant of the motion. Frequently the expression $m[1 - (u/c)^2]^{-1/2}$ is called the 'mass' as distinct from the 'rest mass' m.

The kinetic energy of a mass point is equal to

$$-icq_4 = mc^2[1 - (u/c)^2]^{-1/2}.$$

Thus momentum and energy are—apart from constant factors—components of a four-vector. The component F'_4 of the force is given by

$$F'_4 = \frac{F'_1u'_1 + F'_2u'_2 + F'_3u'_3}{c^2[1 - (u'/c)^2]^{1/2}}$$

This modification of Newtonian mechanics is consistent. Special relativity becomes identical with Newtonian mechanics in the limit of small speeds ($v \ll c$) and its deviations at higher speed have been confirmed by experiment.

Thus it is shown that the ideas underlying the ordinary vector methods are applicable in wider fields of physics than they were originally designed for. In fact their applicability is by no means restricted to the special theory of relativity.

CHAPTER 10

MATRICES IN CLASSICAL STATISTICAL MECHANICS

41. Introduction

The mathematics required for formulating the principles of classical statistical mechanics does not include matrices or abstract vectors. These concepts are, however, used in applications of the general theory to specific objects. An example is considered in this chapter; it concerns the thermal properties of mixed crystals.

If a simple cubic lattice is formed by atoms of two kinds they may alternate regularly along the lattice points in the direction of the crystallographic axes. Alignments of this kind are stable at low temperatures, if at all. If it is known which kind of atom occupies any given lattice point the kind of atom occupying any far away lattice point can be inferred with a probability markedly higher than 50%. This state of affairs is briefly called 'long-distance order'. At higher temperatures some of the order is lost on account of local irregularities; a residual long-distance order will still persist, as the regions of irregularity are enveloped by well aligned regions. Beyond a certain 'critical' temperature all long-distance order vanishes. The probability for any lattice point being occupied by one or the other kind of atom is 50% whatever may be known of other lattice points not in the immediate surroundings. The collapse of long-distance order occurs abruptly with increasing temperature and is called an 'order–disorder transition'. It is accompanied by anomalies in the specific heat and other thermodynamic quantities.

A similar transition occurs at the Curie point where ferromagnetic bodies become paramagnetic. This is connected with the long-distance alignment of electronic spins and its break-down at higher temperatures.

In attempting to establish a quantitative theory of these phenomena some simplifying assumptions are usually made which are not too remote from reality. It is assumed that alignment is exclusively due to the interaction of atoms which are nearest neighbours in the lattice. Every lattice point is endowed with a configurational variable which can take two values only, usually defined as ± 1. They correspond to the kind of atom occupying the lattice point or to the orientation of the spin. If the variables at two neighbouring lattice points are equal to each other (1, 1 or -1, -1), they are to contribute an amount $-\varepsilon$ to the energy: if they differ from each other (1, -1 or -1, 1) they are to contribute an amount ε to the energy. In the present case ε will be assumed to be negative. The contributions of all pairs of neighbours in the lattice are to add up to a configurational energy E_c which is independent of the kinetic and potential energies of lattice vibrations. The values of the configurational variables are not to affect the entropy of the crystal, so that every configuration of the crystal occupies the same amount of phase volume.

It may be noted that the relation between the values of the configurational variables and the configurational energy is of an uncommon kind. Every contribution of $\pm\varepsilon$ depends upon the values of two different variables and every variable is an influence in a number of different contributions.

There are 2^N different configurations of which every one makes a definite contribution to the energy. It is the main object of the theory to find the thermal energy and specific heat of the crystal. The probabilities of the configurations are equal to $\exp(-E_c/kT)$, where T is the absolute temperature and $k = 1{\cdot}371$ erg/degC is Boltzmann's constant. The thermal energy is to be obtained as that expectation of energy determined by the probability distribution. It is to be derived by way of the partition function

$$\zeta(T) = \sum \exp(-E_c/kT)$$

the sum being taken over all configurations. The thermal energy is equal to

$$kT^2 \frac{\partial}{\partial T}(\log \zeta)$$

It is possible to deduce the partition function successfully only for the two-dimensional net of atoms which is used as a model for a crystal lattice. This is shown in the following sections. Extensive use will be made of matrix algebra. In this chapter certain special types of matrices will be used again.

42. Formal solution

Consider a rectangular net of m chains with n sites in every chain. The energy of interaction is denoted by $\pm\varepsilon'$ if it concerns pairs of atoms within a chain and by $\pm\varepsilon$ if it concerns pairs of atoms in different chains. At first ε' and ε are supposed to differ from each other. A one-dimensional periodic boundary condition is adopted by assuming that the atoms in the mth chain interact with the atoms in the first. Every chain has 2^n possible configurations; let them be labelled by numbers ν (or μ) which may be equal to $1, 2 \ldots 2^n$. Configurations of different chains are denoted by distinguishing between $\nu(1)$, $\nu(2) \ldots \nu(j) \ldots \nu(m)$. Every set of these numbers denotes a configuration of the whole net. The relative probability of the configuration ν is equal to $\exp(-E_\nu/kT)$ where E_ν is its configurational energy. Let the probability of the configuration be denoted by $u(\nu, \nu)$; in order to indicate configurations of the first chain the notation $u[\nu(1), \nu(1)]$ is used. If the first and second chain are considered jointly the joint probability of a configuration $\nu(1)$ and $\nu(2)$ is equal to

$$u[\nu(1), \nu(1)]\, v[\nu(1), \nu(2)]\, u[\nu(2), \nu(2)]$$

where the second factor takes account of the interaction of the atoms in the two chains and the resulting effect on the joint probability.

Continuing a third, fourth and eventually an mth chain are added. The joint probability for the configurations of all chains is the probability of a configuration of the net. It is given by the expression

$$u[\nu(1), \nu(1)]\, v[\nu(1), \nu(2)]\, u[\nu(2), \nu(2)]\, v[\nu(2), \nu(3)] \ldots u[\nu(m), \nu(m)]\, v[\nu(m), \nu(1)] \tag{42.1}$$

If use is made of the Kronecker symbol $\delta(\mu, \nu)$ we have

$$u[\nu(j), \nu(j)] = \sum_{\mu(j)} u[\mu(j)\, \nu(j)]\, \delta[\mu(j), \nu(j)] \tag{42.2}$$

The partition function of the net is equal to the sum of expressions (42.1) with respect to all possible values of $\nu(1), \nu(2) \ldots \nu(m)$. Taking account of (42.2) this can be expressed as

$$\zeta = \sum_{\nu(1)} \cdots \sum_{\nu(m)} \sum_{\mu(1)} \cdots \sum_{\mu(m)} \prod_{j=1}^{m} u[\mu(j), \nu(j)]\, \delta[\mu(j), \nu(j)]\, v[\nu(j), \mu(j+1)] \tag{42.3}$$

where $\nu(m+1) = \nu(1)$ and $\mu(m+1) = \mu(1)$.

This expression is readily interpreted as an instance of matrix multiplication. Let $\mathbf{V}$ be a matrix with the elements $v(\nu, \mu)$ and $\mathbf{U}$ a diagonal matrix with the non-vanishing elements $u(\nu, \nu)$. Then the product of the first three factors in (42.3) summed with respect to $\nu(1)$ results in an element of the matrix $\mathbf{UV}$. The whole product summed with respect to $\mu(2) \ldots \mu(m)$, $\nu(1) \ldots \nu(m)$ yields a diagonal element of $(\mathbf{UV})^m$. The last summation with respect to $\mu(1)$ gives the trace of $(\mathbf{UV})^m$ or $(\mathbf{VU})^m$. If m is a large number the trace of $(\mathbf{UV})^m$ can be replaced by the mth power of the largest eigenvalue of $\mathbf{UV}$.

The deduction of this eigenvalue is not merely a problem of diagonalization but also of constructing the two matrices.

43. Expressions for matrices

In the arguments of the preceding section reference is made to matrices $\mathbf{U}$ and $\mathbf{V}$ but they have not yet been defined; they should have 2^n rows and columns. These matrices will now be expressed in terms of other matrices of the same number of dimensions but of greater simplicity.

In equation (10.1) matrices in two dimensions have been defined and denoted by $\mathbf{I}$, $\mathbf{Y}$ and $\mathbf{Z}$. Repeated direct multiplication of these matrices is now used for defining matrices of 2^n dimensions.

$$\begin{aligned} \mathbf{Z}_r &= -\mathbf{I} \times \mathbf{I} \times \ldots \times \mathbf{I} \times \mathbf{Z} \times \mathbf{I} \ldots \times \mathbf{I} \\ \mathbf{Y}_r &= \mathbf{I} \times \mathbf{I} \times \ldots \times \mathbf{I} \times \mathbf{Y} \times \mathbf{I} \times \ldots \times \mathbf{I} \end{aligned} \tag{43.1}$$

In these expressions the rth factor is $\mathbf{Z}$ or $\mathbf{Y}$ respectively; $r = 1 \ldots n$.

The matrices $\mathbf{Z}_r$ are diagonal. Every diagonal element corresponds to a configuration of a chain. They can be divided into two classes, e.g. those in which the configurational variable at r has the values 1 and -1 respectively. The diagonal elements of $\mathbf{Z}_r$ have the same value (± 1) as the configurational variable at r. The matrix $\mathbf{Z}_r\mathbf{Z}_{r+1}$ is also diagonal. Its diagonal elements are 1 if the configurational variables at r and $r+1$ are equal to each other; the diagonal elements are -1 if the configurational variables at r and $r+1$ are unequal. It follows that the diagonal elements of $-\mathbf{Z}_r\mathbf{Z}_{r+1}$ are equal to the contribution of the sites r and $r+1$ to the configurational energy. The diagonal matrix elements of $\mathbf{Z}_r\mathbf{Z}_{r+1}$ are in every diagonal element equal to the value of the total configurational energy of the chain in one of its configurations.

The matrix $\mathbf{U}$ is diagonal and its diagonal elements must be equal to $\exp(-E_\nu/kT)$. It follows that

$$\mathbf{U} = \exp\,(a' \sum_r \mathbf{Z}_r\mathbf{Z}_{r+1}) \tag{43.2}$$

where

$$a' = \varepsilon'/kT \tag{43.3}$$

The matrix elements of $\mathbf{V}$ are conditional probabilities. They express the probability of chain configurations when the configuration of the neighbouring chain is known but they do not take account of the effect on probability of the configurational energy of the chain itself. The matrix $\mathbf{V}$ is constructed by considering a row of lattice points across the chains. Let $f(s, 1)$ and $f(s, -1)$ be the probabilities with which the configurational variable at the point in the chain s takes the values ± 1 respectively. The corresponding probabilities for the point in the chain $s + 1$ are then determined by

$$f(s+1, 1) = f(s, 1)\, e^{a} + f(s, -1)\, e^{-a}$$
$$f(s+1, -1) = f(s, 1)\, e^{-a} + f(s, -1)\, e^{a}$$

where $$a = \varepsilon/kT \qquad (43.4)$$

Thus the neighbouring points in the chains s and $s + 1$ contribute to the matrix $\mathbf{V}$ a sub-matrix

$$\begin{bmatrix} e^{a} & e^{-a} \\ e^{-a} & e^{a} \end{bmatrix} = [e^{a}]\mathbf{I} + [e^{-a}]\mathbf{Y} \qquad (43.5)$$

It is convenient to express $\mathbf{V}$ in terms of a function of a rather than in terms of a itself. The function is denoted by b, and

$$\tanh b = e^{-2a} \qquad (43.6)$$

Taking account of (20.13) expression (43.5) becomes

$$(2 \sinh 2a)^{1/2}[(\cosh b)\mathbf{I} + (\sinh b)\mathbf{Y}] = (2 \sinh 2a)^{1/2}\, e^{b\mathbf{Y}} \qquad (43.7)$$

The matrix $\mathbf{V}$ consists of sub-matrices such as (43.5) about the leading diagonal; all elements outside the sub-matrices vanish. A matrix of this kind is equal to the m-fold product of matrices

$$[e^{a}]\mathbf{J} + [e^{-a}]\mathbf{Y}_r$$

where $\mathbf{J}$ is a unit matrix in 2^{n} dimensions. Then, by (43.7)

$$\mathbf{V} = (2 \sinh 2a)^{m/2} \exp\,(b \sum_r \mathbf{Y}_r) = (2 \sinh 2a)^{m/2}\, \mathbf{W} \qquad (43.8)$$

where

$$\mathbf{W} = \exp\,(b \sum_r \mathbf{Y}_r) \qquad (43.9)$$

The partition function of the net is equal to

$$\zeta = (2 \sinh 2a)^{m/2} \gamma^{m} \qquad (43.10)$$

where γ is the largest eigenvalue of

$$\mathbf{WU} = \exp\,(b \sum_r \mathbf{Y}_r) \exp\,(a' \sum_r \mathbf{Z}_r \mathbf{Z}_{r+1}) \qquad (43.11)$$

In attempting to diagonalize $\mathbf{WU}$ it would not be practicable to proceed by the way of the characteristic equation. An indirect approach is required. As a first step, the properties of diagonal matrices which have some similarity with $\mathbf{WU}$ are considered. Matrices of this kind are

$$\mathbf{K}_r = \exp\,(-\tfrac{1}{2} g_r \mathbf{Z}_r) = (\cosh \tfrac{1}{2} g_r)\mathbf{J} - (\sinh \tfrac{1}{2} g_r)\mathbf{Z}_r \qquad (43.12)$$

where g_r are numbers. The diagonal elements are exp $(\pm\frac{1}{2}g_r)$. The product of these matrices is derived:

$$\mathbf{K} = \prod_r \exp(-\tfrac{1}{2}g_r\mathbf{Z}_r) = \exp[\tfrac{1}{2}(\pm g_1 \pm g_2 \pm \ldots \pm g_n)]\mathbf{J} \quad (43.13)$$

Here every set of + and − signs in the exponent appears in one and only one diagonal element. (43.13) is a standard expression for a diagonal matrix in 2^n dimensions.

The unknown diagonalized matrix $\mathbf{WU}$ should be a special instance of (43.13). The above expressions are not suitable for further deductions. This is due to the commutation rules for the matrices $\mathbf{Y}_r$ and $\mathbf{Z}_s$. All pairs of these matrices commute except the anticommuting $\mathbf{Y}_r\mathbf{Z}_r = -\mathbf{Z}_r\mathbf{Y}_r$. It is possible to simplify calculations by substituting for the $\mathbf{Y}_r$ and $\mathbf{Z}_s$ a set of $2n$ alternative variables all pairs of which anticommute. This substitution is carried out in the next section and will prove useful in spite of the somewhat tiresome set of manipulations required.

44. Anticommuting matrices

Consider now the following set of matrices

$$\mathbf{P}_r = -\mathbf{Y}_1\mathbf{Y}_2 \ldots \mathbf{Y}_{r-1}\mathbf{Z}_r$$
$$\mathbf{Q}_r = \mathrm{i}\mathbf{Y}_1\mathbf{Y}_2 \ldots \mathbf{Y}_{r-1}\mathbf{Y}_r\mathbf{Z}_r \quad (44.1)$$

It is readily verified that

$$\mathbf{P}_r^2 = \mathbf{Q}_r^2 = \mathbf{J}; \quad \mathbf{P}_r\mathbf{P}_s = -\mathbf{P}_s\mathbf{P}_r$$
$$\mathbf{Q}_r\mathbf{Q}_s = -\mathbf{Q}_s\mathbf{Q}_r; \quad \mathbf{P}_r\mathbf{Q}_s = -\mathbf{Q}_s\mathbf{P}_r \quad (44.2)$$

and

$$\mathbf{Y}_r = \mathrm{i}\mathbf{P}_r\mathbf{Q}_r; \quad \mathbf{Z}_r = -\mathbf{Y}_1\mathbf{Y}_2 \ldots \mathbf{Y}_{r-1}\mathbf{P}_r; \quad \mathbf{Z}_r\mathbf{Z}_{r+1} = -\mathrm{i}\mathbf{P}_{r+1}\mathbf{Q}_r \quad (44.3)$$

Further

$$(\mathrm{i}\mathbf{P}_r\mathbf{Q}_s)^2 = \mathbf{J} \quad (44.4)$$

$$\exp(\mathrm{i}g\mathbf{P}_s\mathbf{Q}_r) = (\cosh g)\mathbf{J} + (\sinh g)\mathbf{P}_s\mathbf{Q}_r \quad (44.5)$$

where g is any number. If $t \neq r$ and $t \neq s$ all $\mathbf{P}_t$ and $\mathbf{Q}_t$ commute with (44.5).

In terms of the new matrix variables the expressions (43.2) and (43.9) are changed to

$$\mathbf{U}(a') = \prod_r \exp(-\mathrm{i}a'\mathbf{P}_{r+1}\mathbf{Q}_r) \quad (44.6)$$

$$\mathbf{W}(b) = \prod_r \exp(\mathrm{i}b\mathbf{P}_r\mathbf{Q}_r) \quad (44.7)$$

These relations will be used for deriving transformation formulae of an unusual kind. Consider the collineatory transformation

$$\mathbf{M}' = \exp(\mathrm{i}g\mathbf{P}_s\mathbf{Q}_r)\mathbf{M}\exp(-\mathrm{i}g\mathbf{P}_s\mathbf{Q}_r) \tag{44.8}$$

where $\mathbf{M}$ may be any $\mathbf{P}_t$ or $\mathbf{Q}_t$.

If $t \neq r$ and $t \neq s$ it follows from the commutation rules that $\mathbf{M}' = \mathbf{M}$.

If $\mathbf{M} = \mathbf{P}_s$ then

$$\begin{aligned} \mathbf{P}_s' &= [(\cosh g)\mathbf{J} + \mathrm{i}(\sinh g)\mathbf{P}_s\mathbf{Q}_r]\mathbf{P}_s[(\cosh g)\mathbf{J} - \mathrm{i}(\sinh g)\mathbf{P}_s\mathbf{Q}_r] \\ &= [(\cosh g)\mathbf{J} + \mathrm{i}(\sinh g)\mathbf{P}_s\mathbf{Q}_r][(\cosh g)\mathbf{P}_s - \mathrm{i}(\sinh g)\mathbf{Q}_r] \\ &= (\cosh^2 g + \sinh^2 g)\mathbf{P}_s - 2\mathrm{i}(\sinh g\cosh g)\mathbf{Q}_r \\ &= (\cosh 2g)\mathbf{P}_s - \mathrm{i}(\sinh 2g)\mathbf{Q}_r \end{aligned} \tag{44.9}$$

If $\mathbf{M} = \mathbf{Q}_r$ then

$$\begin{aligned} \mathbf{Q}_r' &= [(\cosh g)\mathbf{J} + \mathrm{i}(\sinh g)\mathbf{P}_s\mathbf{Q}_r]\mathbf{Q}_r[(\cosh g)\mathbf{J} - \mathrm{i}(\sinh g)\mathbf{P}_s\mathbf{Q}_r] \\ &= [(\cosh g)\mathbf{Q}_r + \mathrm{i}(\sinh g)\mathbf{P}_s][(\cosh g)\mathbf{J} - \mathrm{i}(\sinh g)\mathbf{P}_s\mathbf{Q}_r] \\ &= (\cosh^2 g + \sinh^2 g)\mathbf{Q}_r + 2\mathrm{i}(\cosh g\sinh g)\mathbf{P}_s \\ &= (\cosh 2g)\mathbf{Q}_r + \mathrm{i}(\sinh 2g)\mathbf{P}_s \end{aligned} \tag{44.10}$$

The transformations $\mathbf{W}\mathbf{P}_r\mathbf{W}^{-1}$, $\mathbf{W}\mathbf{Q}_r\mathbf{W}^{-1}$, $\mathbf{U}\mathbf{P}_{r+1}\mathbf{U}^{-1}$ and $\mathbf{U}\mathbf{Q}_r\mathbf{U}^{-1}$ can be evaluated by means of (44.9) and (44.10); in accordance with the commutation rules the matrices $\mathbf{W}$, $\mathbf{W}^{-1}$, $\mathbf{U}$, $\mathbf{U}^{-1}$ may, for the purpose of these transformations, be replaced by $\exp(\pm \mathrm{i}b\mathbf{P}_r\mathbf{Q}_r)$ and $\exp(\pm \mathrm{i}a'\mathbf{P}_{r+1}\mathbf{Q}_r)$ respectively. It follows that

$$\begin{aligned} \mathbf{W}\mathbf{P}_r\mathbf{W}^{-1} &= (\cosh 2b)\mathbf{P}_r - \mathrm{i}(\sinh 2b)\mathbf{Q}_r \\ \mathbf{W}\mathbf{Q}_r\mathbf{W}^{-1} &= \mathrm{i}(\sinh 2b)\mathbf{P}_r + (\cosh 2b)\mathbf{Q}_r \end{aligned} \tag{44.11}$$

$$\begin{aligned} \mathbf{U}\mathbf{P}_{r+1}\mathbf{U}^{-1} &= (\cosh 2a')\mathbf{P}_{r+1} + (\sinh 2a')\mathbf{Q}_r \\ \mathbf{U}\mathbf{Q}_r\mathbf{U}^{-1} &= -\mathrm{i}(\sinh 2a')\mathbf{P}_{r+1} + (\cosh 2a')\mathbf{Q}_r \end{aligned} \tag{44.12}$$

The two-by-two matrices on the right-hand side of (44.11) and (44.12) will be denoted by $\mathbf{D}(2b)$ and $\mathbf{D}(-2a')$ respectively. The significance of these transformations is considered in the next section.

45. Relations between matrices of different dimensions

The left-hand sides of (44.11) and (44.12) specify collineatory matrix transformations in 2^n dimensions. The right-hand sides have the forms of vector transformations as defined by (19.3). The transformation matrix is complex-orthogonal and of two dimensions—irrespective of the fact that the vector components themselves are higher order matrices.

Let $\boldsymbol{\rho}$ be a vector of $2n$ dimensions with the components $\mathbf{P}_1$, $\mathbf{Q}_1$, $\mathbf{P}_2$, $\mathbf{Q}_2 \ldots \mathbf{P}_n$, $\mathbf{Q}_n$ and apply the transformations (44.11) and (44.12) to all of its components. Then the right-hand sides represent a vector transformation of the form (19.3)

$$\boldsymbol{\rho}' = \boldsymbol{\Phi}(b)\boldsymbol{\rho} \qquad \boldsymbol{\rho}'' = \boldsymbol{\Psi}(a')\boldsymbol{\rho} \tag{45.1}$$

The matrices $\boldsymbol{\Phi}$ and $\boldsymbol{\Psi}$ are complex-orthogonal and consist of n two-by-two sub-matrices about the leading diagonal. The sub-matrices have the elements

$$\begin{bmatrix} \phi(2r-1, 2r-1) & \phi(2r-1, 2r) \\ \phi(2r, 2r-1) & \phi(2r, 2r) \end{bmatrix} \tag{45.2}$$

and

$$\begin{bmatrix} \psi(2r, 2r) & \psi(2r, 2r+1) \\ \psi(2r+1, 2r) & \psi(2r+1, 2r+1) \end{bmatrix} \tag{45.3}$$

where $r = 1 \ldots n$. All elements outside the sub-matrices vanish. The sub-matrices are equal to $\mathbf{D}(2b)$ and $\mathbf{D}(-2a')$ respectively.

By these transformations a specific relationship is established between the matrices $\mathbf{W}(b)$ and the matrices $\boldsymbol{\Phi}(b)$. In particular it follows from (44.7) that

$$\mathbf{W}(b_1)\mathbf{W}(b_2) = \mathbf{W}(b_1 + b_2)$$

On the other hand repeated application of (44.11) shows that also

$$\boldsymbol{\Phi}(b_1)\boldsymbol{\Phi}(b_2) = \boldsymbol{\Phi}(b_1 + b_2)$$

The relations between the matrices $\mathbf{U}(a')$ and $\boldsymbol{\Psi}(a')$ are of a similar kind.

$\mathbf{W}$ and $\mathbf{U}$ are not the only matrices in 2^n dimensions which are related in this specific way to matrices of $2n$ dimensions. In attempting to find the eigenvalues of $\mathbf{WU}$ it is important to identify a $2n \times 2n$ matrix ($\boldsymbol{\Lambda}$) to which the diagonal matrix $\mathbf{K}$ in (43.13) is related in an analogous way, so that a relation between the eigenvalues of $\mathbf{K}$ and $\boldsymbol{\Lambda}$ can be established. If the matrix obtained by diagonalizing $\boldsymbol{\Phi\Psi}$ is a special instance of the matrix obtained by diagonalizing $\boldsymbol{\Lambda}$, the eigenvalues of $\boldsymbol{\Phi\Psi}$ can be used for deriving the eigenvalues of $\mathbf{WU}$.

For this purpose it is necessary to identify a set of $2n$ matrices ($\mathbf{L}_s$ and $\mathbf{N}_r$) which comply with the multiplication rules (44.2) if they are substituted for $\mathbf{P}_s$ and $\mathbf{Q}_r$ respectively. Also the products $\mathbf{L}_r\mathbf{N}_r$ are to be proportional to $\mathbf{Z}_r$. It is not a foregone conclusion that matrices of this kind exist. Their construction is nevertheless simple.

A matrix $\mathbf{F}$ of 2^n dimensions is defined in terms of the direct nth power of the matrix

$$\mathbf{Y} - \mathbf{Z} = \begin{bmatrix} 1 & 1 \\ 1 & -1 \end{bmatrix}$$

so that

$$\mathbf{F} = \mathbf{F}^{-1} = (\tfrac{1}{2})^{n/2}(\mathbf{Y} - \mathbf{Z}) \times (\mathbf{Y} - \mathbf{Z}) \times \ldots \times (\mathbf{Y} - \mathbf{Z})$$

As $(\mathbf{Y} - \mathbf{Z})\mathbf{Y}(\mathbf{Y} - \mathbf{Z}) = -2\mathbf{Z}$ and $(\mathbf{Y} - \mathbf{Z})\mathbf{Z}(\mathbf{Y} - \mathbf{Z}) = -2\mathbf{Y}$ it follows that

$$\mathbf{F}\mathbf{Y}_r\mathbf{F}^{-1} = -\mathbf{Z}_r \quad \text{and} \quad -\mathbf{F}\mathbf{Z}_r\mathbf{F}^{-1} = \mathbf{Y}_r \tag{45.4}$$

Then the matrices $\mathbf{L}_s$ and $\mathbf{N}_r$ are defined as

$$\mathbf{L}_s = \mathbf{F}\mathbf{P}_s\mathbf{F}^{-1} \quad \mathbf{N}_r = \mathbf{F}\mathbf{Q}_r\mathbf{F}^{-1} \tag{45.5}$$

As the multiplication rules (44.2) are invariant with respect to collineatory transformations it follows that the matrices $\mathbf{L}_s$ and $\mathbf{N}_r$ comply with these rules. Also, by (43.1) and (44.3)

$$\begin{aligned} -\mathbf{Z}_r = \mathbf{F}\mathbf{Y}_r\mathbf{F}^{-1} &= \mathrm{i}\mathbf{F}\mathbf{P}_r\mathbf{Q}_r\mathbf{F}^{-1} \\ &= \mathrm{i}\mathbf{F}\mathbf{P}_r\mathbf{F}^{-1}\mathbf{F}\mathbf{Q}_r\mathbf{F}^{-1} \\ &= \mathrm{i}\mathbf{L}_r\mathbf{N}_r \end{aligned} \tag{45.6}$$

Consider the matrices (43.12)

$$\mathbf{K}_r = \exp(-\tfrac{1}{2}g_r\mathbf{Z}_r) = \exp(\tfrac{1}{2}\mathrm{i}\mathbf{L}_r\mathbf{N}_r)$$

By applying the arguments of Section 44, in particular equations (44.8)–(44.11), it follows that

$$\mathbf{K}_r\mathbf{L}_r\mathbf{K}_r{}^{-1} = (\cosh g_r)\mathbf{L}_r - \mathrm{i}(\sinh g_r)\mathbf{N}_r$$
$$\mathbf{K}_r\mathbf{N}_r\mathbf{K}_r{}^{-1} = \mathrm{i}(\sinh g_r)\mathbf{L}_r + (\cosh g_r)\mathbf{N}_r$$

and consequently

$$\mathbf{K}\boldsymbol{\sigma}\mathbf{K}^{-1} = \boldsymbol{\Lambda}\boldsymbol{\sigma} \tag{45.7}$$

where $\boldsymbol{\sigma}$ is a vector with the components $\mathbf{L}_1, \mathbf{N}_1 \ldots \mathbf{L}_n, \mathbf{N}_n$. The elements of the matrix $\boldsymbol{\Lambda}$ are similar to those of $\boldsymbol{\Phi}$; the non-vanishing sub-matrices of $\boldsymbol{\Lambda}$ are equal to $\mathbf{D}(g)$.

The characteristic equation of $\boldsymbol{\Lambda}$ is a product of n quadratic equations each of which is the characteristic equation of a sub-matrix (45.8). The eigenvalues of $\boldsymbol{\Lambda}$ are thus derived from quadratic equations; they are equal to

$$\lambda_{2r-1} = \exp(g_r), \quad \lambda_{2r} = \exp(-g_r) \tag{45.8}$$

From (45.8) and (43.13) the required relation between diagonal matrices in 2^n and $2n$ dimensions is derived. If the eigenvalues of $\mathbf{K}$ are denoted by k_s this relation is given the form

$$\log k_s = \frac{1}{2}\sum_{r=1}^{n} \pm |\log \lambda_r| \tag{45.9}$$

where all possible sets of + and − signs are to be taken in order to find all possible values of k_s.

If the eigenvalues of $\boldsymbol{\Psi}\boldsymbol{\Phi}$ have the form (45.8) the eigenvalues of $\mathbf{U}\mathbf{W}$ are determined by equation (45.9).

46. Partition function

In order to diagonalize the matrix $\mathbf{\Psi\Phi}$ it is to be transformed to a set of sub-matrices about the leading diagonal which have no row or column in common. Both $\mathbf{\Phi}$ and $\mathbf{\Psi}$ are of this form but their sub-matrices do not coincide in rows and columns. Thus $\mathbf{\Psi}$ will be transformed to $\mathbf{\Phi}$; a matrix $\mathbf{\Omega}$ is to be found such that

$$\mathbf{\Psi}(g) = \mathbf{\Omega\Phi}(g)\mathbf{\Omega}^{-1} \tag{46.1}$$

Taking account of (45.2) and (45.3) it is seen that $\mathbf{\Omega}$ must have an 'even' and an 'odd' part

$$\mathbf{\Omega} = \mathbf{\Delta} + \mathbf{\Gamma}$$

with no row or column in common. The even part $\mathbf{\Delta}$ must have diagonal elements in even columns equal to unity and all its other elements must vanish. The elements of $\mathbf{\Gamma}$ must vanish in all even rows and columns; the remaining part is to be real orthogonal and should replace $\mathbf{P}_r$ by $\mathbf{P}_{r+1}$. This matrix is accordingly of a similar type as the matrix $\mathbf{T}$ of Section 30.

$\mathbf{\Omega}$ can be diagonalized by unitary transformation; for obvious reasons its eigenvalues must be the nth roots of unity, i.e. $\eta, \eta^2 \ldots \eta^{n-1}$, where $\eta = \exp(2\pi\mathrm{i}/n)$. Let the unitary transformation matrix be denoted by $\mathbf{\Theta}$. Like $\mathbf{\Omega}$ it must consist of an 'even' and an 'odd' part with no row or column in common. The even part must be unitary in order to transform $\mathbf{\Delta}$, virtually a unit matrix, into itself. Since also the odd part should be unitary the following set of matrix elements is admissible:

$$\begin{aligned}\vartheta(2r, 2r) &= \vartheta(2r-1, 2r-1)\\ \vartheta(2r, 2r-2) &= \vartheta(2r-1, 2r-3)\\ \vartheta(2r, 2r-4) &= \vartheta(2r-1, 2r-5)\end{aligned}$$

The matrix $\mathbf{\Theta}$ can be factorized in the form

$$\mathbf{\Theta} = \mathbf{I} \times \mathbf{\Xi} \tag{46.2}$$

where $\mathbf{I}$ is a unit matrix in two dimensions and $\mathbf{\Xi}$ is a unitary matrix in n dimensions. The matrix $\mathbf{\Phi}$ admits a similar factorization:

$$\mathbf{\Phi}(g) = \mathbf{D}(g) \times \mathbf{J}_n \tag{46.3}$$

where $\mathbf{D}$ is defined by (44.11) and $\mathbf{J}_n$ is a unit matrix in n dimensions.

As direct multiplication and matrix multiplication commute with each other it follows from (46.2) and (46.3) that

$$\begin{aligned}\mathbf{\Theta\Phi} &= (\mathbf{I} \times \mathbf{\Xi})(\mathbf{D} \times \mathbf{J}_n)\\ &= \mathbf{ID} \times \mathbf{\Xi J}_n = \mathbf{DI} \times \mathbf{J}_n\mathbf{\Xi} \qquad (46.4)\\ &= (\mathbf{D} \times \mathbf{J}_n)(\mathbf{I} \times \mathbf{\Xi}) = \mathbf{\Phi\Theta}\end{aligned}$$

Thus it is seen that $\mathbf{\Theta}$ commutes with $\mathbf{\Phi}$.

If the matrix obtained by diagonalizing $\mathbf{\Omega}$ is denoted by $\mathbf{\Omega}'$ we have

$$\mathbf{\Omega} = \mathbf{\Theta}\mathbf{\Omega}'\mathbf{\Theta}^{-1} \quad \mathbf{\Omega}^{-1} = \mathbf{\Theta}\mathbf{\Omega}'^{-1}\mathbf{\Theta}^{-1}$$

It follows from (46.4) that

$$\begin{aligned}\mathbf{\Psi}(a')\mathbf{\Phi}(b) &= \mathbf{\Theta}\mathbf{\Omega}'\mathbf{\Theta}^{-1}\mathbf{\Phi}(a')\mathbf{\Theta}\mathbf{\Omega}'^{-1}\mathbf{\Theta}^{-1}\mathbf{\Phi}(b)\\ &= \mathbf{\Theta}\mathbf{\Omega}'\mathbf{\Phi}(a')\mathbf{\Omega}'^{-1}\mathbf{\Phi}(b)\mathbf{\Theta}^{-1} \qquad (46.5)\end{aligned}$$

In this way the product $\mathbf{\Psi}\mathbf{\Phi}$ is transformed to the required form of separate two-by-two sub-matrices without actually evaluating the transformation matrix. Also a knowledge of the matrix $\mathbf{\Theta}$ is not required; it enters into (46.5) by way of a collineatory transformation and this cannot affect the eigenvalues of $\mathbf{\Psi}\mathbf{\Phi}$. Hence omitting the first and last factor of (46.5) diagonalization is now possible by elementary means. The matrix product

$$\mathbf{\Omega}'\mathbf{\Phi}(a')\mathbf{\Omega}'^{-1}\mathbf{\Phi}(b)$$

consists of sub-matrices of two dimensions with no rows or columns in common. It is merely necessary to diagonalize the sub-matrices. They have the form

$$\begin{bmatrix}\eta^r & 0\\ 0 & 1\end{bmatrix}\begin{bmatrix}\cosh 2a' & \mathrm{i}\sinh 2a'\\ -\mathrm{i}\sinh 2a' & \cosh 2a'\end{bmatrix}\begin{bmatrix}\eta^{-r} & 0\\ 0 & 1\end{bmatrix}\begin{bmatrix}\cosh 2b & -\mathrm{i}\sinh 2b\\ \mathrm{i}\sinh 2b & \cosh 2b\end{bmatrix}$$

$$= \begin{bmatrix}\cosh 2a' \cosh 2b & \mathrm{i}[\eta^r \sinh 2a' \cosh 2b\\ \quad - \eta^r \sinh 2a' \sinh 2b & \quad - \cosh 2a' \sinh 2b]\\ \mathrm{i}[\cosh 2a' \sinh 2b & \cosh 2a' \cosh 2b\\ \quad - \eta^{-r}\sinh 2a' \cosh 2b] & \quad - \eta^{-r}\sinh 2a' \sinh 2b\end{bmatrix}$$

The determinant of the sub-matrices is unity; their trace, denoted by $2\cos\alpha_r$, is equal to

$$2\cos\alpha_r = 2(\cosh 2a')(\cosh 2b) - 2(\sinh 2a')(\sinh 2b)(\cos 2\pi r/n)$$

The eigenvalues of the sub-matrices are equal to $\exp(\pm\alpha_r)$, where r can take any integer value from 1 to n. The eigenvalues are of the form (45.8) with α_r substituted for g_r. The largest eigenvalue of $\mathbf{UW}$ is, in accordance with (45.9), determined by

$$\log\gamma = \frac{1}{2}\sum_{r=1}^{n}\cosh^{-1}[(\cosh 2a')(\cosh 2b) - (\sinh 2a')(\sinh 2b)\cos 2\pi r/n] \qquad (46.6)$$

Equation (46.6) is the answer to the problem of matrix algebra which was formulated in Section 42. Determination of the thermodynamical properties of the crystal requires additional mathematics details of which are given in the original paper by L. Onsager, 1944,

Phys. Rev., **49**, 117. It is not related to matrices, but concerns the evaluation of the sum in (46.6).

In order to obtain the properties of a large crystal lattice the distinction between the two binding energies is abandoned so that $\varepsilon' = \varepsilon$ and $a' = a = \varepsilon/kT$. The partition function per atom is equal to $\zeta^{1/n}$ and determined by

$$\frac{1}{n}\log\zeta = \frac{1}{2}\log\left(\frac{2\sinh 2\varepsilon}{kT}\right) + \frac{1}{2}\sum_{r=1}^{n_1}\cosh^{-1}\left[\frac{\cosh^2(2\varepsilon/kT)}{\sinh(2\varepsilon/kT)} - \cos\left(\frac{2\pi r}{n}\right)\right]$$

In the limit of large n the last term can be replaced by

$$\frac{1}{2\pi}\int_0^\pi \cosh^{-1}\left[\frac{\cosh^2(2\varepsilon/kT)}{\sinh(2\varepsilon/kT)} - \cos t\right] dt$$

The most important result of this theory concerns the specific heat per atom which is found to show a logarithmic infinity at the temperature $T = 0{\cdot}88\varepsilon/k$. Long-distance order breaks down at the same temperature.

The lengthy deductions of this chapter demonstrate the power of matrix methods in a somewhat unusual field.

Chapter 11

Outlook on Quantum Physics

47. Subject of the theory

Distinction between the facts as described by a physical theory and the mathematics employed in that description is never easy. In quantum physics it is even harder, since both, the facts and the mathematical techniques, are of an unusual kind.

In this chapter the mathematics of quantum physics is introduced in such a way that its interpretation is made as simple as possible. Matrix algebra is used as it is particularly suitable for the present purpose. It would, however, not be sufficient for establishing the complete mathematical equipment of quantum physics.

First the experimental foundations of quantum physics will be reviewed; it is assumed that readers are familiar with these so that a compact summary is sufficient.

The wave nature of electromagnetic radiation, in particular of light and of X-rays, is well established by diffraction and interference experiments. Nevertheless the photoelectric effect and Compton effect do not fit the properties of wave fields. Radiation behaves in these effects like a beam of light particles (photons) which carry energy and momentum and transmit these entities to material particles by the way of collisions. In thermal equilibrium the distribution of energy over the frequency spectrum is determined by Planck's law which at high frequencies describes the energy distribution of a photon gas and at low frequencies the energy distribution in an assembly of classical waves.

Electrons, protons and other material particles can be localized and move along trajectories, broadened images of which are observed in cloud chambers. Nevertheless they can penetrate through barriers of energies higher than their own. On interaction with crystal lattices they show interference patterns not different from those of X-rays. They have accordingly wave-like properties.

The internal movement of atoms and other compound systems is restricted to discrete energy levels the existence of which has been demonstrated experimentally by way of collisions with electrons. Energies between levels are apparently not admissible; on the other hand transitions between these levels do occur, whether or not they pass through the intermediate range.

It is usually possible to account for some of the observations in terms of simple models. It seems on the other hand impossible to make these models mutually compatible.

The theory which eventually succeeded in giving a coherent account of all observations and paved the way for new discovery, started from a reinterpretation of the concept of movement, or more generally, of change in time. In classical physics movement of a particle is specified by regarding the position vector as a continuous function of the time; variations of other mechanical or electrical quantities are specified in terms of continuous time functions. In quantum physics a dynamical variable is either a constant of the motion—such as the energy of a conservative system—or it is indeterminate. Indeterminacy replaces any continuous variation in time. The numerical value of an indeterminate quantity can be found by measurement to any desired accuracy. However, the result of a measurement does not determine the outcome of any future measurement and is not determined by any measurement in the past. On the other hand the results of repeated measurement of constants of the motion are regarded as predictable. Constants of the motion can be measured without interfering with their constancy. In contrast the measurement of any indeterminate quantity would render also the constants of motion indeterminate, at least for a limited time.

Thus the theory has to answer the question what is the probability that an observable will take any particular value under given experimental conditions. In this context the question arises whether the possible values of the energy or of any other dynamical variable are restricted and, if so, to which values they are restricted.

These questions will be partially answered in the next section.

48. Matrix mechanics

Consider a conservative system which consists of one particle or a larger number of particles. The forces may be due to mutual interaction of the particles or to external sources. In classical mechanics the movement of the system is determined by Newton's equations of motion. The energy can be expressed as a function of the coordinates and components of momentum of the particles

$$E = H(q^{(1)}, q^{(2)} \ldots p^{(1)}, p^{(2)} \ldots)$$

the 'Hamilton function'. By solving the equations of motion the co-ordinates and components of momentum are obtained as functions of the time.

If a system of this kind is to be considered from the point of view of quantum physics the numerical values of the coordinates and components of momentum must not be functions of the time. On the other hand there is reason to believe that the mechanical equations of motion do retain some significance. In order to meet these two requirements the dynamical variables are represented by matrices, in fact Hermitean matrices, which are time dependent and which are related by the mechanical equations of motion.

At this stage no attempt is made to decide whether or not the energy should be restricted to discrete values. Rather, the restriction to discrete levels is accepted as an experimental fact. The energy is then represented as a diagonal matrix with diagonal elements equal to the discrete energy levels of the system. Degeneracy is admitted; thus two or more diagonal elements may be equal to one and the same value of the energy.

Dynamical variables other than the energy are represented by matrices which are usually not of diagonal form. The rows and columns of these matrices correspond to the rows and columns of the energy matrix. If $\mathbf{A}$ is a matrix representing a dynamical variable, element a_{jk} is accordingly connected with two values of the energy E_j and E_k (which in the case of degeneracy may be equal to each other). These matrix elements also depend on the time t and are given by

$$a_{jk} = b_{jk} \exp\,[2\pi i(E_j - E_k)t/h] \qquad (48.1)$$

where b_{jk} is independent of the time and h ($= 6{\cdot}625 \times 10^{-27}$ erg sec) is Planck's constant. Obviously the diagonal elements are time-independent.

It is further assumed that the matrices representing Cartesian coordinates or components of momentum commute with each other, except those pairs representing a Cartesian coordinate and its corresponding component of momentum to which the following commutation rule applies:

$$\mathbf{p}^{(j)}\mathbf{q}^{(j)} - \mathbf{q}^{(j)}\mathbf{p}^{(j)} = (h/2\pi i)\mathbf{I} \qquad (48.2)$$

In fact this commutation rule cannot be satisfied by finite matrices. Fortunately, however, it can apply to finite matrices asymptotically; in a set of matrices of increasing numbers of dimensions it is usually possible to satisfy equation (48.2) everywhere except in a single element the significance of which diminishes with increasing number of dimensions. Thus the results of matrix algebra as obtained in the earlier chapters can be applied.

In order to construct the matrices and derive the energy levels it is possible to proceed in the following way. Coordinate and momentum matrices are constructed in such a way that they comply with the multiplication rules; otherwise their choice is arbitrary. Using the classical Hamilton function the energy matrix is constructed as a function of the coordinate and momentum matrices. The resulting energy matrix can eventually be diagonalized; its eigenvalues are the required energy levels.

This procedure is impracticable. Nevertheless in special instances the deduction of the energy levels is a relatively simple problem.

49. Harmonic oscillator

Let a particle of mass m be bound to a position of equilibrium by a restoring force that is proportional to its negative displacement. Its Hamilton function is

$$H = (p^2/2m) + (2\pi^2 m\nu^2)q^2 \tag{49.1}$$

where m is the mass, q the displacement, p the momentum and ν the frequency. The equations of motion are

$$p = m\frac{dq}{dt}; \quad \frac{dp}{dt} = m\frac{d^2q}{dt^2} = -4\pi^2\nu^2 q \tag{49.2}$$

They are solved in terms of two constants of integration (a and b) by

$$q = a \cos 2\pi\nu t + b \sin 2\pi\nu t \tag{49.3}$$

and the energy is

$$E = 2\pi^2\nu^2(a^2 + b^2) \tag{49.4}$$

and, of course, independent of the time.

In the early stages of quantum theory it had been assumed that the energy is restricted to discrete levels

$$E_n = nh \quad (n = 0, 1, 2 \ldots) \tag{49.5}$$

This was a hypothesis which, in fact, makes the historical origin of quantum theory.

It was further inferred that transitions between these energy levels could occur only in such a way that n increases or decreases by unity.

It will now be shown that the theory of the harmonic oscillator can be derived as a special instance of matrix mechanics as laid down in the preceding section. The Hamilton function is to be regarded as a matrix, being a function of the matrices $\mathbf{p}$ and $\mathbf{q}$. By (23.C) the eigenvalues of **H** must be non-negative as it is proportional to the sum of two Hermitean matrices with non-negative eigenvalues.

On account of the rule for differentiating matrices (cf. Section 5 and exercise 3, Chapter 1) and by (48.1) the second time derivative of the matrix **q** is given by a matrix $\ddot{\mathbf{q}}$ consisting of the elements

$$\ddot{q}_{jk} = -4[\pi^2(E_j - E_k)^2/h^2]q_{jk}$$

so that equation (49.2) turns into

$$4\pi^2\{-(E_j - E_k)^2/h^2 + \nu^2\}q_{jk} = 0 \qquad (49.6)$$

It follows that the diagonal elements q_{jj} must vanish, and that non-diagonal elements q_{jk} also vanish unless

$$E_j - E_k = \pm h\nu \qquad (49.7)$$

However, not all elements of the coordinate matrix can be zero. For this reason the eigenvalues of **H** must have the constant difference shown on the right-hand side of (49.7) and take the form of an arithmetic progression. There must be a lowest energy E_0 because negative eigenvalues of **H** are ruled out (cf. 23.C).

The elements of the coordinate matrix vanish except for q_{10}, q_{21}, q_{32} . . . and q_{01}, q_{12}, q_{23} . . . The coordinate and momentum matrices are related by equations (48.2) and (49.2). According to the latter equation the elements p_{jk} vanish unless q_{jk} differs from zero. Combining both equations it follows that

$$m\left(\frac{d\mathbf{q}}{dt}\mathbf{q} - \mathbf{q}\frac{d\mathbf{q}}{dt}\right) = \frac{h}{2\pi i}\mathbf{I}$$

or

$$\frac{2\pi i m}{h}\sum_l [(E_j - E_l)q_{jl}q_{lk} - (E_l - E_k)q_{jl}q_{lk}] = \frac{h}{2\pi i}\delta_{jk}$$

The diagonal element of this equation reduces to

$$|q_{n(n+1)}|^2 - |q_{n(n-1)}|^2 = h/8\pi^2 m\nu \qquad (49.8)$$

as all other terms in the sum vanish. On account of this equation the moduli square of the elements of the q-matrix form an arithmetic series which continues to infinity without any gap. It must, however, have a lowest term since the moduli square could not be negative. This term is equal to

$$|q_{01}|^2 = h/8\pi^2 m\nu \qquad (49.9)$$

The elements of **q** determine the elements of **p**. If (49.1) is interpreted as a matrix equation and **q** and **p** are inserted it may be concluded that the eigenvalues of equation (49.8) form an unbroken arithmetic series from the lowest value to infinity.

The lowest energy level is determined by

$$E_0 = \sum_k [(\tfrac{1}{2}m)p_{0k}p_{k0} + 2\pi^2\nu^2 q_{0k}q_{k0}]$$
$$= (\tfrac{1}{2}m)\,|\,p_{01}\,|^2 + 2\pi^2\nu^2\,|\,q_{01}\,|^2 = \tfrac{1}{2}h\nu \qquad (49.10)$$

so that

$$E_n = (\tfrac{1}{2} + n)h \quad (n = 0, 1 \ldots) \qquad (49.11)$$

This is similar to the original conjecture of (49.5), the difference being the 'zero-point energy', which prevents the oscillating particle from reaching a state of rest.

The coordinate and momentum matrices consist of the elements

$$q_{(n+1)n} = q^*_{n(n+1)} = \frac{1}{2}\left[\frac{h(n+1)}{2\pi^2 m\nu}\right]^{1/2} \exp(2\pi i\nu t + i\beta_n)$$
$$(49.12)$$
$$p_{(n+1)n} = p^*_{n(n+1)} = \frac{i}{2}[2hm\nu(n+1)]^{1/2} \exp(2\pi i\nu t + i\beta_n)$$

where the β_n are real but otherwise arbitrary phase constants.

In this way the deduction of the energy levels and construction of the coordinate matrix are completed.

It may be noted that the non-vanishing elements of the coordinate matrix correspond to those pairs of levels between which transitions are admissible. The reason for this coincidence is a relation between transition probabilities and the moduli of matrix elements; its deduction would require greater details of the theory than can be presented here.

50. Interpretation

So far matrices have been introduced in a formal way. Physical meaning was attached only to the eigenvalues of the energy matrix which are shown to be the admissible energy levels of the quantum mechanical system.

The diagonal elements of matrices with non-vanishing elements off the diagonal admit another simple interpretation. If $\mathbf{A}$ represents a dynamical variable a, the elements a_{jj} are the statistical expectation of a, on the assumption that the energy is E_j. In terms of observations the meaning is as follows.

First the object is brought to such conditions that its energy is E_j; this can, if necessary, be checked by measurement. Subsequently a is measured and the result is recorded. By the process of measurement the energy has been changed. Thus, before repeating the measurement of a the object has to be restored to the energy E_j; only then is the measurement of a repeated. If a number of measurements have been taken the arithmetic mean of the results should be equal to a_{jj}.

If the energy is degenerate, the same procedure is possible if the control of the energy is supplemented by the control of alternative constants of motion.

Non-diagonal elements of matrices do not determine the expectation of dynamical variables but they contribute to the expectations of the higher powers. Even more important is their relation to transition probabilities and collision cross sections; these relations are, however, neither of a general kind nor could they be derived by any simple argument.

Additional means of interpretation are available if unitary transformations are admitted. The transformation matrices may depend upon the time. The transformed energy matrix is no longer diagonal and the time dependence of the transformed matrices is, in general, not sinusoidal. By transformations of this kind matrices other than the energy matrix can be diagonalized. Their eigenvalues are interpreted as the possible results of the measurement of the dynamical variable which the matrix represents.

Consider again the above repeated measurements of the dynamical variable a. Let $\mathbf{U}$ be unitary and let $\mathbf{A} = \mathbf{U}\mathbf{A}'\mathbf{U}^{-1}$ where $\mathbf{A}'$ is a diagonal matrix. Then

$$a_{jj} = \sum_k u_{jk} a'_{kk} u^{-1}_{kj} = \sum_k a'_{kk} \mid u_{jk} \mid^2 \tag{50.1}$$

As a_{jj} is the statistical expectation of a random variable which can take the values a'_{kk}, and since $\mid u_{jk} \mid^2$ satisfies $\mid u_{jk} \mid^2 \geqslant 0$ and

$$\sum_k \mid u_{jk} \mid^2 = 1 \tag{50.2}$$

the coefficients $\mid u_{jk} \mid^2$ are interpreted as probabilities. They determine the probability that the value a'_{kk} is obtained in any measurement of a when it is known that the energy is E_j. In the conventional terminology $\mathbf{U}$ is the transformation matrix from the 'eigenstates' of a to the eigenstates of the energy. The term 'eigenstate' signifies conditions in which the measurement of a dynamical variable yields with certainty a specified result. If the transformation matrix can be deduced from the theory, the above set of measurements is better determined than if only a_{jj} were known. The elements of the transformation matrix determine the probability distribution of all possible results of the experiment.

However, the above methods cannot cater for dynamical variables which are not restricted to discrete values and therefore do not give a complete picture. An alternative approach is outlined in the following.

Matrices representing dynamical variables can be transformed in such a way that they become independent of the time. In this case the change in time of the mechanical system is fully determined by the change in time of the transformed matrix.

Introductions to quantum mechanics usually start with a time-independent representation of dynamical variables. The change in time is specified in terms of a time-dependent 'wave function' $\psi_j(x, t)$. This is a complex function of the $3N$ coordinates of N particles of which the mechanical system consists. Let this set be denoted by x. Also the wave function is associated with a discrete energy level of energy E_j. By means of multipliers which are independent of the coordinates it is possible to normalize the wave functions in such a way that

$$\int |\psi_j|^2 \, dx = 1 \tag{50.3}$$

the multiple integral being taken over the whole range of the $3N$ coordinates.

Although these functions bear no resemblance to matrices they play in fact the part of transformation matrices, transforming from eigenstates of particle positions to eigenstates of the energy. The normalization rule (50.3) is analogous to (50.2). The interpretation of wave functions is similar to the interpretations of transformation matrices. $|\psi_j(x, t)|^2 \, dx$ is the joint probability for the positions of the particles if the energy is equal to E_j.

Dynamical variables are represented by operators involving differentiation of the wave function with respect to the coordinates and multiplication of the wave function into known functions of the coordinates. The wave functions are determined by a partial differential equation known as Schrödinger's wave equation. This kind of mathematics has little in common with that of the preceding section. The interpretations are, however, virtually the same as before. If $\mathscr{A}$ is the operator representing the dynamical variable a the expression

$$a_{jk} = \int \psi_j^*(x, t) \mathscr{A} \psi_k(x, t) \, dx$$

(ψ_j^* being the conjugate complex to ψ_j) is an element of the matrix $\mathbf{A}$ so that the interpretation of operators is reduced to the interpretation of matrices. In particular the diagonal elements

$$a_{jj} = \int \psi_j^*(x, t) \mathscr{A} \psi_j(x, t) \, dx$$

are again the statistical expectations of a if E_j is the energy. (If the level E_j is degenerate it is associated with two or more wave functions; it may, however, be possible to identify any particular one of these functions by recording the value of the energy and some other constants of motion.)

If $\mathscr{H}$ is the operator representing the Hamiltonian and if the wave functions comply with the conditions

$$\mathscr{H}\psi_j = E_j\psi_j$$

and

$$\int \psi_k^* \psi_j \,\mathrm{d}x = \delta_{kj}$$

the energy matrix is a diagonal matrix with the admissible energy levels in the diagonal.

The mathematical methods for setting and solving these equations are outside the scope of this book. This preview of quantum physics has accordingly to be concluded at this stage.

Unitary transformations, matrix elements, traces and eigenvalues are standard concepts in quantum physics. For this reason matrix algebra plays in the physics of the present times a similar role as the calculus played in the physics of the eighteenth and nineteenth century.

Index